DO YOU KNOW HOW TO
FLIRT?
IS YOUR CRUSH CRUSHING BACK?
WHAT'S YOUR IDEAL
GUY TYPE?
20 LOVE QUIZZES TO SET YOUR HEART STRAIGHT

BY THE EDITORS AT ALLOY.COM

ALLOY BOOKS
Published by the Penguin Group
Penguin Putnam Books for Young Readers,
345 Hudson Street, New York, New York 10014, U.S.A.

Published by Puffin Books,
a division of Penguin Putnam Books for Young Readers, 2001

10 9 8 7 6 5 4 3 2 1

Copyright © 17th Street Productions, an Alloy Online, Inc. company, 2001
All rights reserved

Cover design by Lauren Monchik

 Produced by 17th Street Productions,
an Alloy Online, Inc. company
33 West 17th Street
New York, NY 10011

Alloy, Alloy.com, AlloyBooks, and 17th Street Productions and associated logos
are trademarks and/or registered trademarks of Alloy Online, Inc.

ISBN 0-14-131318-8
Printed in the United States of America

table of contents

Crushing. Flirting. Dating. Analyzing. Obsessing. Overanalyzing. Some call it love; you call it confusing.

Don't sweat it. When it comes to love, everyone gets confused. And while you might be tempted to ask anyone and everyone for advice—from your best friends to strangers on the street—we've come up with a better solution. The editors at Alloy.com have whipped up a bunch of love quizzes based on the very questions you've asked in your letters and your message-board posts and in the chat rooms. And since you've helped make these quizzes so popular on the website, we've collected them and put them all in this awesome book.

So the next time you find yourself wondering about the best way to get a guy to notice you or what to do when you start dating a guy that your friends absolutely hate or how to deal when two guys are sweating over you after a semester-long dry spell, stop. You can skip the stressing, grab the nearest pencil, and start decoding the mystery that is your love life! ♥

are you clueless
about love?

Do you know what's going down when it comes to matters of the heart? Or do you have no clue what to do when faced with a crush-worthy cutie? Take this quiz to find out how you rate in the love department. ♥

1. **You notice your crush staring at you from across the cafeteria. You:**

   a) Acknowledge your hottie with a wave, smile, or a nod.

   b) Make eye contact, then swiftly look away as soon as you realize you've just turned roughly the color of cherry Kool-Aid.

   c) Immediately run to the bathroom to locate the huge piece of spinach in your teeth that must have caught his attention.

2. You're on-line when your crush's SN pops up on your buddy list. You:

a) IM him right away. And if he doesn't answer right away, IM him again—something like, "Hey, why are you ignoring me?"

b) Keep your on-line presence to yourself but follow him from chat room to chat room, becoming jealous every time he chats with anyone with a female-sounding SN.

c) Give him a few minutes to check his e-mail or whatever, then IM him a quick, "How R U?"

3. You've hung with your crush a few times and you've even held hands and kissed once or twice. In your book that means the two of you are:

a) Officially dating. You might as well be the first on his speed dial. He might as well be wearing a T-shirt that says, "Hands off, ladies! I'm taken."

b) Overdue for a what's-going-on-with-us? convo.

c) People who have locked lips. Sure, it'd be great if he wanted something more, but who are you to put pressure on the sitch?

4. You and your BF get into your first fight ever about his obsession with fantasy football. This obviously means:

a) Nothing. You'll be back to snuggling before *That '70s Show* comes on.

b) It's so over.

c) You two can practice the "communication exercises" you read about in *Cosmo Girl* last week.

5. When trying to figure out if that cute guy in drama club is crushing back atcha, you:

    a) Figure out a way to become his scene partner, drop a few flirty clues, and gauge the sitch by his flirt-back ratio.

    b) Corner him during your vocal warm-up and ask, "Are you gonna ask me out already?"

    c) Get your BFF to pass him a note asking what he thinks of you and then pore over his reply, obsessively examining his every word.

6. Do you believe in love at first sight?

    a) Yes. When it's right, it's right.

    b) Does the first time you saw Brad Pitt count?

    c) Yes. You also believe in Santa Claus and that aliens built the pyramids.

7. You think being in love means:

    a) One more chance to have your heart smashed to pieces and smeared all over the floor by some uncaring boy's Vans.

    b) You will never spend another moment unhappy.

    c) You never have to worry about having something to do on a Saturday night—and you always have someone rad to hang with!

8. Of these choices, who is the most romantic movie couple?

    a. Zach and Laney (*She's All That*).

    b. Jack and Rose (*Titanic*).

    c. Billy and Sidney (*Scream*).

9. One of your (really cute) close guy friends says he only thinks of you as a friend, but he's always holding your hand and givin' you hugs. Not that you mind. You:

a) Slip a little flirty-flirty his way and see if he bites.

b) Take his word for it. Hey, if he wanted anything more, he'd make a move, right?

c) Think of any reason at all for him to give you frequent back rubs. Constantly talk about how he'd be the perfect boyfriend. He'll come around.

10. You call your BF after <u>The Real World</u>, like you do every week, and his phone is busy. You:

a) Don't think twice. He's probably in the middle of downloading some bazillion-megabyte fighting game.

b) Imagine him flirting with other girls on-line and get angrier and angrier until you decide that when he finally calls you, you're gonna break up with him.

c) Call his mom's line and make her put him on. What was he thinking? It's ten thirty-two! If he didn't want you waking up his mom, he should've called like he was supposed to.

scoring

1. a-2, b-3, c-1

2. a-3, b-1, c-2

3. a-3, b-1, c-2

4. a-2, b-1, c-3

5. a-2, b-3, c-1

6. a-3, b-1, c-2

7. a-1, b-3, c-2

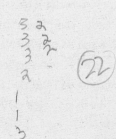

8. a-2, b-3, c-1
9. a-2, b-1, c-3
10. a-2, b-1, c-3

are you clueless about love?

Standing in Your Own Way (10–16)

You are totally overthinking this whole love thing. Instead of going with the flow, you have a tendency to get all worked up over minutiae, panic, and then abort mission before things run their course. Jeez, you're like the black cat crossing the path of love, baby. Chill out, would ya? Here's the deal: Instead of sucking the spontaneity out of your relationships by obsessively overanalyzing them, you should experiment in trying to allow yourself to enjoy the moment. This tiny attitude adjustment might send your love quotient skyrocketing!

Clued in Like Cupid (17–24)

You're definitely clued in when it comes to crushin'. You make guys feel comfortable because you're comfortable with them. You can tell when a look's just a look and when it means, "Hey, baby, can I have your number?" And you can read the signs when someone loves to love ya, even if it's not as obvious as Christina Aguilera's dye job. So, keep on doin' that thing you do. And don't be afraid to share the wealth with a few of your less love savvy friends. They'll thank you for it.

Hopeless Romantic (25–30)

You have this fairy-tale picture of what love is about, and it just ain't happening with the guys you're hanging around. Well, don't ya think your expectations are a little unrealistic? Listen here, sister—Prince Charming will have bad table manners, sing way off-key, and say the wrong thing roughly 40 percent of the time. That's 'cause boys are human, too. You can't expect your love life to unfold like in the movies—without a hitch or a commercial break. Relationships go through ups and downs. Love isn't all candlelit dinners and stargazing on the grass. The sooner you learn to accept that, the happier you'll be in the long run!

do you know how to flirt?

You never know when you're gonna get the chance to make an impression on a guy. Seriously, you could encounter a hottie anywhere—and you've gotta be prepared. So take this quiz to find out if you're ready to work it—or about to blow it. ♥

1. It's Saturday night, and you and your girlfriends are hangin' at a massive end-of-the-year bash. Some random (but cute) guy interrupts to ask where the bathroom is. You:

   a) Point to the huge line down the hall—without even looking at him—and go on chatting with your crew.
   b) Say you don't know (while rolling your eyes) and turn back to your friends.
   c) Offer to show him where it is—you were just about to get in line yourself.

2. You're browsing the racks at Flipside Records when you notice the hottest hottie of them all working behind the counter. You:

    a) Buy a stack of CDs and pray that he'll notice how infinitely cool you are from your taste in music.

    b) Ask him if the new Moby CD is any good while he's stuffing your purchases in the bag.

    c) Tell him you're looking for a gift for a friend and get him to ditch register duty to help you pick something out.

3. Because you're a good friend, you've accompanied your BFF on her family picnic. Bonus! Her older bro's bud is a dead ringer for James Van Der Beek. To get his attention, you:

    a) Introduce yourself, and start a conversation. What the heck, you've got to be more interesting than your BFF's dorky cousins, right?

    b) Make eyes at him while you're passing the potato salad.

    c) Try to look bored from across the picnic blanket. Maybe he'll come over if he's bored, too!

4. Rock on! Metallica tickets went on sale at nine this morning! It's 9:05, and you're in line, hoping to score tix for you and your crew. When the hot head banger in front of you turns around and asks for the time, you:

    a) Blurt it out fast and then wait for him to ask for your number.

    b) Tell him and say how you hope the line moves fast— you were bummed when the first concert sold out in a nanosecond!

c) Give it to him, mention missing the show last time, and then offer to lend him the *Metallica Behind the Music* you taped the other night. He can call you if he wants to borrow it.

5. **You're at the skate park when you spot a new dude, crankin' out ollies. You decide to:**

a) Stand back and silently watch the hottie from afar.

b) Go up to him and ask where he bought his sweet board.

c) Give him props for his skatin' skills and ask him to show you a trick or two.

6. **Argh! You're up to your elbows in nonfat chocolate at the Yogurt Shack when your crush walks in. When he places his order, you:**

a) Smile and say hi, but make his strawberry cone in record time, without stopping for small talk. You're too busy to flirt!

b) Smile, take a deep breath, try not to stress over the long line, and try to have a semi-normal conversation.

c) Have your coworker help him—you've got hot fudge in your hair!

7. **You've found that the surefire way to get a guy to notice you is:**

a) To deliver a fierce pickup line—the wittier the better!

b) To talk to him normally—you know, like a friend would.

c) To primp for at least an hour before leaving the house—to make sure you're always looking fly.

8. You're at the mall with your crew when you run into the cutie you secretly drool over in homeroom. You:

    a) Say hi and make small talk for a few minutes.

    b) Say hi and tell him about the party that you're going to that night.

    c) Ask him if he's going to the party and then offer to give him a lift 'cause your mom's driving a bunch of friends.

9. All aboard! You're taking the Eastern Express to visit your aunt who lives two hours away. When a good-looking guy sits down next to you on the train, you:

    a) Ask him where he's headed.

    b) Steal glances at him while pretending to read your *Rolling Stone*.

    c) "Accidentally" trip over him on your way to the dining car.

10. You're totally working it on the dance floor when, out of the blue, a guy comes up and asks you to dance. You:

    a) Giggle, turn red, and say, "I dunno." Then turn to look at your buds.

    b) Say okay, dance with him for one song, and then make up an excuse to go back to your friends.

    c) Say, "Sure—but can you shake it like Ricky Martin?"

11. Give yourself one point for each of these flirtation tactics you've used:

    a) Asked a guy for the time—after stashing your watch in your bag.

b) Flirted with someone while on the clock at your job.

c) Approached a guy you noticed checking you out.

d) Used the look-over-look-away-look-over-again technique on someone you spotted on the street.

e) Pretended you thought a cute stranger was someone you actually knew—just so you could chat him up.

f) Laughed at a guy's joke—even if it was weak.

12. Subtract one point for each of the following flirting flubs you've made:

a) Avoided talking to a crush because you weren't looking your best.

b) Avoided talking to a crush because you were with your mom/dad/little brother/etc.

c) Stopped your conversation with a hottie to introduce him to another girl.

d) Blew off a guy who approached you because you were with your friends and couldn't be bothered.

e) Kept your mouth zippered during a group convo because you couldn't think of anything good to say.

f) Relied on telepathic vibes to get a guy to talk to you.

scoring

1. a-2, b-1, c-3

2. a-1, b-2, c-3

3. a-3, b-2, c-1

4. a-1, b-2, c-3

5. a-1, b-2, c-3

6. a-2, b-3, c-1

7. a-2, b-3, c-1

8. a-1, b-2, c-3

9. a-3, b-1, c-2

10. a-1, b-2, c-3

11. Add one point for each.

12. Subtract one point for each.

do you know how to flirt?

Flirt SOS (10–14)

Is it just us, or is somebody stuck in the '50s? Oh, wait, no, it's you. Get with it, girl! It's 2001, and you're missing out on tons of flirting opportunities. Trust us, they come up all the time—and you can never anticipate when. So you have to be ready to roll with 'em. So be alert, and be open to meeting new guys. Don't automatically give 'em the brush-off just because you're busy or hangin' with your friends. And don't expect to always be approached—if you spot someone you want to get to know, don't just stand there; bust a move! It's a lot easier than you think.

On Flirt Alert (15–25)

Okay, you've got a pretty good grasp on this whole flirting thing. You know that you can't just sit there and wait for a guy to make a move. You can't use your powers of telepathy to get someone to notice you. And sometimes you even have to work it a little. You've got those basics nailed, but now you need to take these skills to the next level. Meaning that you need to learn how to spot not-so-obvious flirting opportunities and react to them quickly. So you won't be kicking yourself after you've just bought a stack of CDs from the cute record store guy—without exchanging so much as a word.

Ready, Aim, Flirt! (26–36)

Get down with your bad, flirty self! You're always ready to work it—whether you're at school, at the mall, at the supermarket, wherever. You know that it's quite possible to encounter a cool guy just about anywhere. So, you're always prepared. Not that you're perpetually glammed out or have a bunch of corny pickup lines memorized. You're just always aware of what's going on, and more important, who's got it goin' on. And you're not passive, either. You know that the best way to flirt is to get a real conversation going and then take it from there. With your pro approach, you're totally open to meeting new guys and giving them the opportunity to get to know you.

who's your ideal
zodiac crush?

Sure, you look in those astrology books and they tell you who to scope based on what your sign is. But what good is that? They should ask you what's important to you, then hit you up with the knowledge of what sign to pursue. That's where we come in.

Answer the questions to reveal which sign you should scope. ♥

1. Your fantasy dude asks you out on a date. What's he say?
   a) "Hey! Wanna go for a hike and take along a picnic?"
   b) "I would love to just hang out and talk. Up for that?"
   c) "How about hitting Colossus this afternoon?"
   d) "I don't care what we do . . . as long as we do it together."

2. When it comes to fashion, your ideal crush is all about:
   a) Keepin' it real. Real simple. T-shirts, jeans, and sneakers.

b) Style, baby. Style. This guy keeps up.

c) It changes. One day he's a ruffneck, the next a prep.

d) Fashion? That's sooo not important to your ideal crush.

3. If your crush had only <u>one</u> extracurricular activity, what would it be?

a) Sports. Sports, sports, sports.

b) Peer counseling.

c) Just one? Impossible! My crush has about thirty-five extracurriculars! And he's president of all of them!

d) How do you spell "J-O-B"?

4. Everyone's got a favorite type of music. What's your boy's?

a) Hip-hop or metal. And he likes it loud.

b) Love songs. What can he say? He's a sap.

c) Okay, not everyone's got a favorite type. He likes it all.

d) Whatever it is, it's gotta be relaxing. Music is for chilling.

5. It's your birthday. What does your boy give you?

a) Flowers, chocolate, and more flowers. You know, the classics.

b) A mix tape of our favorite songs and a homemade card. Awww.

c) Something he had to break his piggy bank for.

d) Nothing. He knows his presence is present enough for me.

6. If your crush was a movie star, who would he be?

a) All rough and tough like Russell Crowe.

b) All romantic like Freddie Prinze, Jr.

c) All hilarious like Adam Sandler.

d) All sweet like Jason Biggs.

7. Bummer for your fantasy man: He's stuck with you, your sister, and your mother, watching <u>Steel Magnolias</u>. How does he deal?

a) He squirms and whimpers until you let him go.

b) As long as you're holding hands, he doesn't care!

c) He cracks jokes the whole time, and as much as you don't want to, you can't help laughing!

d) He loves this movie.

8. Pick a crush, any crush:

a) The strong, silent one.

b) The organized one.

c) The focused one.

d) The sensitive one.

e) The sexy one.

f) The mysterious one.

g) The impulsive one.

h) The leader.

i) The one who's smirking.

j) The comedian.

k) The confident one.

l) The ingenious one.

scoring

1. a-1, b-2, c-3, d-4

2. a-1, b-2, c-3, d-4
3. a-1, b-2, c-3, d-4
4. a-1, b-2, c-3, d-4
5. a-1, b-2, c-3, d-4
6. a-1, b-2, c-3, d-4
7. a-1, b-2, c-3, d-4
8. a-1, b-2, c-3, d-3, e-2, f-3, g-1, h-2, i-3, j-1, k-2, l-3

who's your ideal zodiac crush?

(8–9) Your match: Taurus.

Key words: *Dependable, brave, and picky.*
If you need someone you can count on no matter what, call a Taurus.

See, they're always on time, always well prepared, and always ready to pitch in and help out. And they've always got nice things to say about others. But the bull tends to be stubborn, and no matter how hard you try, you'll never get him to do something he doesn't want to do.

(10–11) Your match: Virgo.

Key words: *Organized, articulate, and in the know.*
Need a crush that's always on the ball? Nab yourself a Virgo. They never break a date, they're first on the phone for tickets to that show you wanted to see, and they never, ever run out of gas in the tank. But beware the Virgo if their plans don't pan out. They tend to make you feel like it's your fault, even when it isn't.

(12–13) Your match: Capricorn.

Key words: *Focused, energetic, and clear.*

Got a question? Ask a Capricorn. Because even if they don't know the answer (which is seriously unlikely), they'll know how to find out, pronto. Date a Capricorn and he'll have a plan when he asks you out. None of this, "I don't care— whatever you want to do!" Break a date with a Capricorn, however, and forget being forgiven.

(14–15) Your match: Gemini.

Key words: *Versatile, social, and funny.*

Geminis are all about one thing: communication. That means they're up-front, they're honest, and they love to share what's going on in their lives. They've got tons of friends because they connect with everyone. But the thing is, even though they always say what they want to say, they always say something different. Geminis are constantly changing their minds.

(16–17) Your match: Libra.

Key words: *Confident, peaceful, and balanced.*

Need a little harmony in your life? Sit next to a Libra. Famous for keeping things light and sweet, Libras like every-one to get along. Especially in love! The problem? You might never be sure exactly what's on your Libra's mind. They tend to blow off what they're really feeling just to keep conflict away.

(18–19) Your match: Aquarius.

Key words: *Unique, ingenious, and independent.*

Bored with being bored? Good thing your match is an Aquarius. Because no matter what you're doing, from watching Road Rules to acting it out, an Aquarius will make it seem like all kinds of fun. Fact is, they can't stand things any other way. Be prepared to cut this crush some slack, though—Aquarians have a tendency to flake out.

(20–21) Your match: Cancer.

Key words: *Sensitive, caring, and thoughtful.*
On the lookout for the sweet, sensitive type? Then net yourself a Cancer because they're all over that tip. Yep . . . if it's picnics in the park instead of house parties all night long, then a Cancer's your catch. But watch out: Cancer can turn crabby at the drop of a hat—you'll never find a more moody mate.

(22–23) Your match: Scorpio.

Key words: *Direct, powerful, and exciting.*
Three-hour telephone conversations. Daylong hand-holding sessions. Loud, possibly off-key love serenades. Scorpios are, in a word, intense. And chances are that Scorpio you've got your eye on is flirting right back at ya. The problem? He's probably flirting with a bunch of other people, too.

(24–25) Your match: Pisces.

Key words: *Compassionate, empathetic, and mysterious.*
Chances are that the silent hottie who sits alone at lunch (but doesn't seem to mind at all) is a Pisces. And how did he know your name before you even introduced yourself? Yep, Pisces have incredible intuition and seem to understand

things before the rest of us. But you might have to pin this one down, literally, to get a straight answer sometimes. They aren't always known for being clear.

(26–27) Your match: Aries.

Key words: *Enthusiastic, impulsive, and original.*
Like surprises? You'll like Aries. They're always up for something new, always energetic and exciting, and they never wait around for things to happen. They make them happen. But don't expect a whole lot of patience from an Aries. They'll do anything to keep from being bored, including cause trouble.

(28–29) Your match: Leo.

Key words: *Generous, charming, and magnetic.*
Date a Leo, and be prepared for an amazing ride—Leos don't do anything halfway, and they don't do anything quietly. Usually very popular, Leos have plenty on their schedules all the time, and they want everyone to participate. But know this: Leos like to be in charge. That means most of the time, it's their way or no way. Be prepared to follow.

(30–31) Your match: Sagittarius.

Key words: Understanding, clever, and a little wacky.
Spend a day with a Sag, and it'll feel like three. See, they bounce from one fun thing to the next, with few worries about where they've been or where they're going. They're more interested in fun than rules. Which is great! That is, unless you're looking for a lock-down relationship. Sags tend to roam.

is your BF **hiding something?**

Take a good look at that boy you're going out with. How well do you really know him? Sure, you've got all his digits, you know what's he's into and what makes him freak, you've got the 411 on his family and friends, and you're pretty sure you know where he spends his after-school hours. But something tells you there's more to him than that. Is there? Take our quiz and clue in. ♥

1. **The last time your boyfriend invited you over to his place, it was because:**
  a) His grandmother was in town, and he really wanted you to meet her.
  b) His parents were out of town, and he wanted your help cooking dinner for his younger sisters.
  c) He's never invited you over.

2. **It's been a long, hard week, and you're psyched it's**

almost over. You definitely want to spend some time with your boyfriend this weekend, so you ask him if he's free Saturday night. His response:

    a) "Um, I'm not sure. Maybe I'll call you or something."

    b) "Nope, I'm not. But we could hang out Saturday afternoon if you want."

    c) "You know it! Pick you up at seven-thirty?"

3. Does your boyfriend screen his phone calls?

    a) Always. In fact, he doesn't pick up even when it's someone he wants to talk to.

    b) No way! My dude picks up on the first ring.

    c) Sometimes, but you're pretty sure he's never screened yours.

4. Homecoming's around the corner, and you've decided to ask him to go. He:

    a) Totally falls all over himself apologizing for not asking you first. Then promises to make it up to you.

    b) Says, "Sure. That could be cool."

    c) Goes off on how he thinks all school functions like that are bogus and how he'd never want to support such a lame event by showing up.

5. How would you describe the last three dates you've had?

    a) Does sneaking in the back door of his house and helping him clean out his garage count as a date?

    b) Not bad, but did they all have to include spilling every single one of his guts? Enough with sharing your feelings, dude!

c) Pretty good. Except that one date where he ran into this random girl from his past and ended up leaving the movie halfway through.

6. You tried to page him last night, but you couldn't get through—his beeper never picked up. How does he explain it?

a) "Don't worry. I changed my beeper number last week. I'll give you the new number later on. Or something."

b) "I know. I think I might have left it in your basement."

c) "Really? No way! I wonder if my batteries died?"

7. It's your three-month anniversary, and you decided to surprise him with a special homemade chocolate cake—just the two of you. Success?

a) What an awesome night. He even showed up with a present for you—a really cool mix tape with all your favorite songs! You played it during dinner.

b) When you were like, "Happy anniversary!" he was like, "Listen, could you not tell anyone that it's our anniversary? In fact, could you not tell anyone we're going out?"

c) Even though he had to reschedule twice, you two had a pretty good time.

8. Has your boyfriend ever asked you to "cover" for him? As in, lie for him?

a) Like, every other day.

b) Maybe a couple of times, come to think of it.

c) Heck no! He's sooo honest!

9. Knock him down a notch for each lame excuse he's used to break a date with you (check all that apply).

   a) "I have to walk my dog."

   b) "But we just went out last week!"

   c) "My mom's not feeling well. Again."

   d) "I have to help a friend with a math project."

   e) "We had a date?"

   f) "I don't have anything to wear."

   g) "My bud really needs me tonight. He's having a hard time."

   h) "I have a paper due in like three weeks."

scoring

   1. a-1, b-2, c-3

   2. a-3, b-2, c-1

   3. a-3, b-1, c-2

   4. a-1, b-2, c-3

   5. a-3, b-1, c-2

   6. a-1, b-3, c-2

   7. a-1, b-3, c-2

   8. a-3, b-2, c-1

   9. Give yourself one point for each.

is your BF hiding something?

Straight-Up Now (8–14)

This boy is an open book, and you've got your reading glasses on, don't ya? There's no place he goes that you haven't been and no one he talks to who you don't know.

And there's nothing he does that he doesn't give you a complete play-by-play about. Honesty rules, and it rules that you can totally trust him, but think about this: Wouldn't it be cool if he left something to the imagination? A little mystery goes a long way.

Slightly Shady (15–21)

Sure, he might be hiding *something* from you, but then again, who said everything should be your business in the first place? After all, the poor guy is allowed *some* privacy. If his sneakiness really starts to get in the way, well, kick the boy to the curb, but first, check your head: Isn't there something you might be hiding from him, too? Maybe?

Liar, Liar (22–32)

Your dude is obviously hiding something from you. But the question is, what is it? Could it be another girlfriend? Or is it more like a past probation violation? Or maybe it's just the fact that he likes Chunky Monkey while Totally Nuts is more your speed. Consider a confrontation. (Don't assume you know what he's keeping on the down-low, but be aware that there's something down there. After all, some things are private, and that's okay.)

are you **boy crazy?**

Do you have boys on the brain 24/7? Or can you actually go to the deli without reapplying your lip gloss on the off chance that the cashier may be an Ashton Kutcher look-alike? Take this quiz to find out if you've gone completely boy batty! ♥

1. **You're scarfing down curly fries at the diner when your crush compliments you on your polka-dot halter top. You:**

    a) Make your BFF come back with you to the mall the next day so you can buy five more in all different colors.

    b) Smile, say, "Thanks," and feel like a supermodel for the rest of the night.

    c) Shoot him a cheesy grin, then obsess for the next forty-eight hours over why he liked the shirt. The color? The cut? Why?

2. **At a pool party you're most likely to be:**

a) Hanging on a lounge chair with your BFF, whispering about a cutie you spotted across the water.

b) Poolside, lounging in your bikini and making eyes at all the hotties.

c) Splashing around with your crew. So what if your hair frizzes up? Parties are for having fun.

3. **Your bio grade is hurtin'—bad. When it's time to choose lab partners, you pick:**

a) The funny guy who sits behind you. At least he can make you laugh through icky frog dissection.

b) That Josh Jackson look-alike; you know, the one who's cruisin' for an F. Summer school isn't such a bad thing.

c) The smartest guy in class. Who cares if he smells like chloroform?

4. **Your crew has planned to meet for a Saturday afternoon matinee. As you swipe on the last touch of lip gloss, you get a call from the cute guy you met at the pool. He asks you to meet him at the bowling alley—in half an hour. You:**

a) Say, "Sure!" and eighty-six your movie plans without a second thought.

b) Tell him, "Today's a no go, but maybe tomorrow?"

c) Say, "No prob, but we'll have to make it quick this time—I'm meeting my crew later."

5. **You swoon for boy bands, but you find out your crush is way into Slipknot and Kittie. You:**

a) Declare Nick Carter dead in your eyes and rush out to buy a scary mask.

b) Chalk it up to an opposites-attract thang.

c) Toss your copy of "No Strings Attached" in your underwear drawer and start occasionally listening to the hard rock station.

6. **You meet a really cool guy at a party. When it's over, you casually toss him your phone number. The next day you:**

a) Meet your BFF for lunch at McDonald's and proceed to describe every detail of your encounter with Mystery Man, from his adorable mussy hair to his love of poetry. You maintain hope that a message from lover boy is waiting on your machine when you get home.

b) Stay planted in your bedroom all day, mere inches from the phone. Announce that no one in your family is allowed to go on-line lest you miss his call.

c) Go to the beach with your friends, as planned. Sometime between tanning your back and getting a Popsicle, you wonder if he called.

7. **You think about guys:**

a) From the minute you brush your teeth in the morning till you lay your head on your pillow at night.

b) When there's a cute one in the vicinity.

c) If you hear a romantic song, see a hot CK ad, or pass the boys' gym class.

8. **You're heading to the Video Barn with your little bro to get a movie to watch while you baby-sit. You:**

a) Hop onto your bike in the same stained sweatpants you wore when washing the dog.

b) Change into the blue tank top that brings out your eyes and put on some lip gloss. You never know what hotties could be hiding in the Action/Adventure aisle.

c) Make your BFF pick up the flicks for you and drop 'em off. What if someone cute saw you at the video store with your bratty bro?

9. Your oral report is scheduled for today. You:

a) Hope your crush is feeling better. He's missed the past couple of days of school because of a strep throat.

b) Search feverishly for the perfect outfit. This will be the perfect opportunity for you to show off how good you look.

c) Keep rehearsing the Bill of Rights in your head.

10. Have you ever done any of the following? (Check all that apply.)

a) Practiced writing your married name—your first name with the last name "Timberlake."

b) Walked by your crush's house on the off chance that he's outside, checking the mail.

c) Bought a boy band calendar.

d) Made a list of all the guys in class and rated them on a "cuteness" scale.

e) Gone into a chat room under an SN like "HotChick17" lookin' for cute guys.

f) Joined a club or group 'cause it was chock-full o' cuties.

g) Called your crush and hung up.

h) Written "I heart [crush's name here]" on your notebook.

i) Asked a hot guy to teach you to do something you had only marginal interest in (fly-fishing, archery).

j) Hung out somewhere really lame, like the Kmart parking lot, because your crush sometimes skates there.

k) Gotten into trouble just so you could have detention with your crush.

scoring

1. a-3, b-1, c-2

2. a-2, b-3, c-1

3. a-2, b-3, c-1

4. a-3, b-1, c-2

5. a-3, b-1, c-2

6. a-2, b-3, c-1

7. a-3, b-1, c-2

8. a-1, b-2, c-3

9. a-2, b-3, c-1

10. Give yourself one point for each.

are you boy crazy?

The Opposite of Obsessed (9–14)

Congrats! You are a self-confident chickie who'd never deny her own interests to impress a boy, even if he does have a torso like a D'Angelo. Is your crush into goth rock? Great, you can deal, but he won't be seeing you in a fishnet shirt anytime soon. After all, why should you change your taste in music, style, or anything else about you? You know that one isn't the loneliest number. You'd never settle for Mr. Wrong just to have a boyfriend. You're happy with yourself, and that's what counts.

Not Quite Crazed (15–20)

Yeah, so your room has a few Backstreet Boys posters on the walls, and you do have a soft spot for the cutie who works at the skate shop. Still, you'd never bail on a long-time friend in order to smooch with someone who might not be around for the long haul. Your world doesn't revolve around boys!

Boys on the Brain (21–38)

You must chill. You don't just crush on guys—you worship them. You painstakingly plan every moment of your day around your crushes or your potential crushes. Basically, you need to get real. You shouldn't need a boy to make you feel pretty, smart, or talented. Start exploring your own interests more. Take up guitar, in-line skating, or even belly dancing! When you stop worrying about what boys think, you'll be able to be happy whether there are guys around or not!

how **great** was your **date?**

So you finally got what you've been wanting for, like, ever—a date with him. But how well did it actually go? Before you drive yourself crazy doing a mental play-by-play recap of the evening, take this quiz and figure out the real score. ♥

1. When he asked you out, he said he'd pick you up on Saturday at four. What time did he actually ring your doorbell?

    a) Three-thirty.

    b) Three fifty-five.

    c) Four.

    d) Four-twenty.

2. When you came down the stairs to meet your guy, you couldn't help but notice he was wearing:

a) A blink-182 tee, baggy-butt jeans, and a baseball cap. The same exact outfit he wore to school that day.

b) A casual but nice shirt and pants. He definitely made an effort—and he may even have ironed!

c) A tux. No wonder that lady mistook him for the maître d'.

3. After your dad talked his ear off for what seemed like an eternity and you guys were heading out the door, your date said:

a) "Wow! You look great!"

b) "Gee, your old man sure likes to blab!"

c) "Let's roll—we don't want to miss the previews."

4. During the date his beeper went off. What'd he do?

a) Interrupted you—midsentence—to return the call.

b) Ignored it—"Whoever it is can wait."

c) Checked to see who it was, then decided to call them back later.

5. Okay, so there were one or two awkward silences, but for the most part you guys had a pretty decent conversation going. What did you talk about?

a) How much you can't stand your parents—and how your two best friends are totally dissing you these days.

b) The stuff he's into—like his band, his new car, and his pet iguana, Igor.

c) A pretty much fifty-fifty split of stuff you're into and stuff he's into.

6. When you were telling the story about how you were pulled onstage at the Christina Aguilera concert last week, he:

    a) Told you it was a great story—after you finished telling it.

    b) Butted in to tell you all about the time he was pulled onstage at a Metallica show.

    c) Looked disinterested, sneaked a peek at his G-Shock, and yawned.

    d) Exclaimed, "Dang, she's cute!"

7. After the movie you went out for pizza. Be honest. His table manners:

    a) Were excellent—he even put a napkin in his lap.

    b) Were pretty good—except for when he dug his spoon into your sundae.

    c) Were nonexistent. Ew, can you believe he picked his teeth at the table!

8. At the end of the night, when he dropped you off, he:

    a) Said that he had fun and that he'd call you tomorrow.

    b) Said that he had fun and would call you . . . some-time.

    c) Looked at you expectantly—like he wanted you to say you had a good time.

    d) Was kinda awkward.

    e) Took off really fast—like a bat outta hell!

9. Fess up. Did you kiss good-bye?

    a) Yes!

    b) No, but I could tell that he wanted to. . . .

c) No—it wasn't happenin'. Not a chance.

10) Subtract one point for each of the following that he did on your date:
   a) Flirted with the waitress.
   b) Interrupted or changed the subject when you were talking.
   c) Looked bored.
   d) "Forgot" his wallet and stuck you with the bill.
   e) Ordered for you.

scoring
   1. a-2, b-3, c-4, d-1
   2. a-1, b-3, c-2
   3. a-3, b-1, c-2
   4. a-1, b-3, c-2
   5. a-1, b-1, c-3
   6. a-3, b-2, c-0, d-1
   7. a-3, b-2, c-1
   8. a-4, b-2, c-3, d-2, e-1
   9. a-2, b-1, c-0
   10. Subtract one point for each.

how great was your date?

Disastrous Date (4–9)
   Your evening was a total nightmare—from the second he picked you up (in that smelly blink-182 tee, no less) to the moment he dropped you off (and bolted faster than a

world-class sprinter). But you probably didn't mind his hasty getaway since you were looking at your watch all night long. Especially during his half-hour diatribe about his iguana's eating habits. Snore. Yeah, your date was a bust, but that's okay. At least you didn't kiss the toad good night!

Decent Date (10–20)

There were a few awkward moments on your date. Like the millisecond after you caught him looking at your waitress just a little too long. But overall the night was a success and went off without a hitch. He was on time (maybe even a little early) and totally polite. You both had lots to say, neither one of you dominated the conversation, and the whole experience was pretty fun. So did this date establish a love connection? Well, it's a little soon to tell. You may even need a second date—or a third or fourth before you figure that out. Whatever you do, don't wait by the phone!

Dream Date (21–29 points)

Okay, so you were totally nervous, and you're still biting your nails wondering if he's ever gonna call. (Or maybe you should call him?) But believe us, you can chill out a bit—because you had a certifiably great date. A nearly perfect date, in fact! You both were on your best behavior—but still managed not to be too reserved. You managed to have balanced, fun conversations, and you actually learned some stuff about each other, too. And last but not least, you guys had some major chemistry happenin'. Sounds like serious sparks were flying. But then again, you already knew that, right?

what kind of impression will you make on the fam?

It's more traumatic than bathing suit shopping. More agonizing than taking the SATs. We're talking about meeting your BF's parents, of course. No doubt, it's a stressful sitch—but now you can take a trial run before you go and screw it up in person. Take this quiz to find out what kind of impression you'll make on the fam. ♥

1. **You and your BF had plans to see the latest horror flick in the theater, but now he's stuck baby-sitting his little bro. You:**

    a) Ditch the scary movie and score three tickets to *Poké-mon 5: The Cutest Pokémon Fiasco of All Time*. For the next two hours jab your BF with your elbow and whisper "This is the worst night of my life!"

    b) Declare that if his sib is more important to him than the date that the two of you had already etched in stone, he can just spend the night—and the next week—without you.

c) Take little bro to the arcade, win a bunch of dorky prizes at Skeeball, and spend the rest of the evening letting him win at Streetfighter 2.

2. Your BF's mom has invited you to one of her famous meatball dinners. One prob—you're a vegetarian. You:

a) Take the first opportunity to go on a huge tirade about how barbaric it is to murder defenseless animals for consumption.

b) Eat around the meatballs while shooting your BF dirty looks across the table.

c) Cop to your veggie status but declare all side dishes deelish! After dinner sneak out for a bean burrito with your BF.

3. By dessert you've already:

a) Knocked a serving spoon onto the floor three times and said, "Ew, you guys drink milk with spaghetti?"

b) Begun exchanging recipes with his mom.

c) Had your elbows on the table for the better part of an hour.

4. Upon entering his house, his Shih Tzu, Rocky, immediately leaps on top of you, licking you feverishly and snagging your leopard-print tights. You:

a) Shriek, "Get that thing *off* me!"

b) Grit your teeth, smile, and say, "Isn't Rocky cute?" Then excuse yourself to the bathroom and commence scrubbing wildly to rid yourself of any dog cooties.

c) Pet Rocky's head until he calms down. Ditch the stockings, and go on with the evening as planned.

5. It's his great-grandmother's hundredth birthday, and they're throwing her a party. You wear:

a) A white cotton tee and long skirt and closed toe shoes. The shoes are a must since you don't want to give Grams heart failure if she catches a glimpse of your black glitter toenail polish.

b) A backless tank, snakeskin skirt, and knee-length boots. Well, you'll be going out *afterward*, right? She's ancient—how late can she possibly stay up, anyway?

c) Something dressy, which you translate to mean "all black." On your way out the door your mom calls out, "This is her birthday party, not her funeral, right?"

6. At a fancy family function one of your jelly bracelets catches on a serving spoon, splashing dark red punch all over their immaculate white lace tablecloth. You:

a) Are so mortified that your face turns roughly the same shade as the punch stain. You burst into tears and make a run for the bathroom.

b) Grab a napkin and try that cleaning trick you learned from Martha Stewart using lemon rinds and ice water. The next day you send over a bouquet of flowers with an apology.

c) Laugh it off and continue with your conversation. Jeez, you hope they have a good dry cleaner.

7. You refer to your BF's parents as:

a) Mr. and Mrs. Fill-in-their-last-name.

b) Bob and Carol.

c) Quasimodo and Cruella De Vil.

8. Your BF calls and says his dad's been sent to the hospital for a kidney stone operation. You:

a) Run out and get him a get-well-soon card and some of those gross coffee-flavored sucking candies he's so into. At least when he comes out of surgery, he'll have something nice waiting for him.

b) Tell him to send his dad a feel-better shout out for ya.

c) Say, "Yowch, that sounds painful!" Then tell him about the really funny thing that happened at the mall today.

9. Have you ever smooched in front of his parents?

a) Yeah, all the time.

b) Just the occasional peck good night.

c) Uh, no way. Hand holding is the most PDA his 'rents will ever see from you.

scoring

1. a-2, b-1, c-3
2. a-1, b-2, c-3
3. a-1, b-3, c-2
4. a-1, b-2, c-3
5. a-3, b-1, c-2
6. a-1, b-3, c-2
7. a-3, b-2 c-1
8. a-3, b-2, c-1
9. a-1, b-2, c-3

what kind of impression will you make on the fam?

Rude and Crude (9–18)

If you wanna start seeing the welcome mat when you go over to your BF's house, you're gonna have to put in a little work. That means you should probably leave the attitude at home. Think of his fam as an extension of him—and ya like him enough, right? Listen, his parents might not love ya, but they don't have to hate you, either. So stop pushing their buttons, okay?

Makin' Yourself at Home (19-22)

Yeah, so you've never done anything as grotesque as cursing or belching in front of your BF's fam, but a few social graces have been overlooked in your dealings with them. The 'rents are just people, not demigods, so you shouldn't live in mortal terror of them. But you also shouldn't go overboard on the we're-all-equals-here tip. They're the ones who spawned the guy you smooch, so you should give 'em props for that. It's the little things that'll earn ya brownie points with his parents. Things like buying his dad a get-well card when he's sick or sending his mom flowers when you ruin her tablecloth send the message that you care. And admit it—you do.

Manners Matter! (23-27)

Talk about the kinda girl a guy can bring home to Mom— you're the epitome! You're no stranger to the idea of respect—you know when to keep your outfits G rated and when to keep your crazier opinions to yourself. You've got manners the likes of which people don't see outside of charm school. Congrats! You have enough common sense to keep you on the fam's good side. Uh, just make sure not to overdo it, or you'll look like a kiss up.

do you **lead people** on?

When it comes to dealing with the opposite sex, are you straight up or are you shifty? Take this quiz to find out if you lead people on. ♥

1. **Mike has a killer crush on you, but you only like him as a friend. So of course you:**

    a) Are really sweet to him but never in more than a we're-just-buddy-buddy sorta way.

    b) Flirt mercilessly with him, especially when there's someone you actually think is cute in the vicinity.

    c) Call him whenever your plans fall apart. You know he'll always be there, pitifully hangin' by the phone.

2. You're crushin' on Eddie, but his best friend, Mike (from question 1—ugh!), has just asked you out. You:

   a) Say no, of course. You're holding out for the real deal.

   b) Say yes, of course. More time with Mike means more time with Eddie!

   c) Say yes, of course. You can always dump him once Eddie realizes he's in love with you.

3. You dissed your last BF pretty hard core about two months ago, and he's been moping around ever since. But during the homecoming game, you see him snuggling up to some chickie in the bleachers. You:

   a) Feel a few pangs of jealousy. But you're over it in, like, four seconds.

   b) Go up to the couple long enough to get a good look at her and whisper in his ear about how you still think about him all the time and you'll call him later. Squeeze in an intimate cheek kiss if there's time.

   c) Wave hello and give him a thumbs-up when she's not looking. She seems cool—good for him!

4. How often do you say you're gonna call but don't?

   a) Only when the guy is really annoying. Or when he stops doing your math homework for you. Or when you meet someone cuter.

   b) Never. Why would you say that to someone if you didn't mean it?

   c) Occasionally. But only after your date has gone really badly and you're dying to get home so you can call your friends and rank on him.

5. When there are two potential BFs in the picture, you deal by:

    a) Deciding which one has more staying power and sticking with him.

    b) Hangin' with both of them until one does something to annoy you.

    c) Working the sitch so they're insanely jealous of each other. A brawl in the school yard would be so Helen of Troy.

6. How do you greet your guy friends when you see 'em?

    a) Yell, "What's up, loser?" and stick your tongue out.

    b) Scream, "Ohmigod, hiiiii!," body slam them with a full-contact hug, and stick 'em with a big ol' cheek kiss.

    c) Smile, say, What's up?," and give 'em a shoulder-contact-only hug.

7. Your on-line crush IMs you, asking if you have a boyfriend (you do). After careful consideration you type:

    a) Not really. Howbout U?

    b) Yeah, he rocks! Check out his profile—his SN is Rock57.

    c) Why, do you wanna be my BF?

8. You're at a party, sitting next to a cute guy. You have a Diet Pepsi in one hand. What are you doing with your other hand?

    a) Alternately twirling your hair and playing with your straw.

b) Resting it on his forearm. Hey, you had to get his attention!

c) Wiping the soda you spilled on your skirt off with a napkin.

9. That quasi-dorky guy in your chem class asks you to go to the sold-out D'Angelo concert with him this weekend. You:

a) Say, "Sure!" You're bound to run into some hotties at the show. And you can always ditch him. Hey, it's not like he's your boyfriend or anything.

b) Agree to go. I mean, it's not like he's full-on dorky. And it is gonna be a good show. If he doesn't start looking cuter when the lights dim in the amphitheater, you'll always have D'Angelo to look at.

c) Tell him thanks, but you have other plans. He might be disappointed at first, but maybe he'll end up taking another girl who'll really appreciate it.

10. You and your best guy friend (who's been in love with you since the second grade) have long-standing Saturday night movie plans. How many times have you canceled?

a) Without fail, every time something better has come up.

b) Once or twice, but only when there was a really cute guy involved in your plan.

c) Never! He's one of your best buds, and these movie nights are one of the reasons it's stayed that way for all these years.

scoring

1. a-1, b-2, c-3
2. a-1, b-3, c-2
3. a-2, b-3, c-1
4. a-3, b-1, c-2
5. a-1, b-2, c-3
6. a-1, b-3, c-2
7. a-3, b-1, c-2
8. a-2, b-3, c-1
9. a-3, b-2, c-1
10. a-3, b-2, c-1

do you lead people on?

100 Percent Honest (10-13)

You're so conscientious of other people's feelings that it's amazing no one's ever checked you for circuitry. Actually, we're just dissing you 'cause we're jealous. See, it would never even cross your mind to make plans with a guy who's crushin' on you just 'cause you didn't have anything better to do. As a matter of fact, you'd rather spend the night watching BattleBots with your little brother than watching some guy you weren't into give you puppy dog eyes. And that total lack of wishy-washiness will get you mad props in the end. You go!

Mixed Messages (14-22)

You're not totally heartless—just a little selfish. Like, you'd never actually lie about whether you had a BF or not—but you might forget to mention him for a while. And you'd never intentionally use a guy who likes you as a backup plan for Saturday night—but you might cancel with him if something better comes along. You should watch the signals you send a little better. 'Cause one day you might find yourself in his Dr. Martens. That's when you'll realize that being on the receiving end of those mixed signals really rots.

Miss Leading (23-30)

Hey, did you just wink at us? Well, hey, we think you're kinda cute, too. Wait a minute—now, see, this is your whole problem. You give out more signals than an air traffic controller! Listen—it's just not cool to play games with people's hearts. You know that guy you consider "just a friend"? Or that guy you think is "just okay" from your science class? Well, imagine ripping their hearts out of their chests, throwing 'em on the floor, and stomping up and down on 'em with those three-and-a-half-inch platforms. That's what you're doing if you continue with the flirty-flirty even though you know it'll never happen between you two.

do you blow off your friends for guys?

You love your friends. You love your boyfriend. But when push comes to shove, are you one of those girls who'd dis their friends for a guy? Take this quiz and find out! ♥

1. **Who do you hang with most of the time?**

    a) Your girlfriends. Guys are great and all, but a true friend is worth a hundred of 'em.

    b) Large groups of girls and guys. You're practically guaranteed a good time that way. Besides, the bigger the group, the bigger the chance that some fine young thing is representing.

    c) The boys. Girls can be so . . . catty.

2. Summer is over, and you know what that means: Your crew is reinstating its Friday night video-slumber party, and you're totally psyched. Until the cute new guy asks you over to his house to help catch him up in Spanish. You:

    a) Say you're sorry; you've got plans. But make sure to say it with an apologetic smile.

    b) Tell him you've already planned to go to video night, but tell him that he's welcome to join you as long as he doesn't mind watching a chick flick.

    c) Give him your phone number and bat your eyelashes. Your friends will totally understand, won't they?

3. You just started dating the most amazing guy—and you're well on your way to becoming that twosome everyone else uses as an example of the perfect couple. And not only is he cool, so's his whole posse. What do you do next?

    a) Throw a party. If your friends hit it off, you can chill as a group!

    b) Hang out with your BF whenever you can. He doesn't go to your school, so every free second you can be together is important. It doesn't matter who else is around.

    c) See him when both of your schedules mesh. You have a life, and you're not giving it up for anyone!

4. You've been on the phone with your sobbing friend (who just caught her BF cheating) for over an hour when you get a call-waiting beep. It's the guy you kissed two weeks ago; you know, the one you've been praying would call. You:

a) Tell him you're in crisis-intervention mode and get his phone number. Call him back as soon as your friend moves from grief into anger.

b) Click back to your friend and tell her that it's a long-distance call for your mom and you'll call her back ASAP. Then spend the next five hours on the phone with the boy.

c) Rush the guy off the phone by telling him to call back in an hour. If he really likes you, he'll understand and call back. Your friend needs you!

5. One Tuesday at lunch you and your friends make the common realization that you need to get your hands on those wild-patterned T-shirts everyone's wearing. So you set Saturday aside for some serious shopping. But just as you're running out on Saturday morning, your boyfriend calls and asks if you want to hang. You:

a) Tell him to meet you at the mall. He likes all your friends and thinks shopping with you is amusing. This way you get to see all of your favorite people at once!

b) Tell him you're on your way out and you'll call him back when you can. You have plans, and you're not gonna break them for some guy—even if he is the best-looking guy in the whole school!

c) Tell him you're going shopping with your crew, but you should be home around five. Maybe you guys could hang out then?

6. What are most of the notes you send in class about?

a) How bored you are, how much school sucks, how much you wish you were sitting on a beach some-where, and how disgusting the neck pimples on the guy who sits in front of you are.

b) The crisis du jour. Between you and your four best friends, there's always somebody freaking out about something.

c) Boys, boys, and more boys. Either how much you wish you had a BF, how annoying your BF is, how he did or didn't call, or how confusing the whole dating thing is. You may be in history class, but it feels like you're studying alien psychology.

7. You start dating a guy that your friends absolutely hate. Whaddaya do?

a) Spend Friday night with your friends and reserve Sat-urday for the boy. It stinks that you have to split your life like that. But nobody ever said having everything was easy.

b) Dump the guy. The combined instincts and brainpower of your friends can't possibly be wrong. After all, they were right about passing on those burgundy velvet pants. You only wish you had listened then, too!

c) Get into a fight with your friends. They know how important your BF is to you, and they still dis him all the time! If they're gonna be so obnoxious, you'll just spend your time with people who actually respect you!

8. It's your parents' fifteenth anniversary, and your uncle's throwing a big, fancy party for them. You and your sister can both bring guests. Who're you going to ask?

   a) Your BFF. She's been to so many of these things, it's like she's a member of the family. How could you not invite her?

   b) Your new BF. Who cares if you've only been dating a week! There's gonna be an old skool big band playin', and you want to dance with someone who's not your dad.

   c) Both your BF, your BFF, and her boyfriend. The four of you are gonna have a blast!

9. How did you meet your last boyfriend?

   a) Okay, well, first your BFF liked him, but then when you tried to get the scoop on his feelings for her, like, the two of you just started hitting it off.

   b) As a favor to your BFF, you agreed to meet her boy's cousin. The two of you went out a couple of times, but you're not sure you'd call him a boyfriend.

   c) Through a friend. Her boyfriend's brother is on a hockey team, and you went to a game, met the team afterward, and the rest was, like, history!

10. How did your friends react to your last breakup?

   a) They went into full-support mode. They even bought you those special tissues with the lotion in them so nobody at school would know you'd been crying!

   b) They started asking you to hang out more. After all, without the boyfriend you had twice as much time on your hands, and they knew you'd be miserable home alone.

c) They comforted your now ex-boyfriend. They were more his friends, anyway.

scoring

1. a-1, b-2, c-3
2. a-1, b-2, c-3
3. a-2, b-3, c-1
4. a-2, b-3, c-1
5. a-3, b-1, c-2
6. a-1, b-2, c-3
7. a-2, b-1, c-3
8. a-1, b-3, c-2
9. a-3, b-1, c-2
10. a-1, b-2, c-3

do you blow off your friends for guys?

Girls, Girls, Girls (10–15)

You're a great friend . . . too great, in fact. Not only do you not blow off your friends for guys, you never leave your friends. Period. And while all that focus on lifelong buds is great, it's also an easy way to avoid more anxiety-inducing things. Like, say, boys. Can you say uncool? Your friends don't want you to blow off a guy just so you can rush back to solving their crises. They don't want you to dump your boyfriend just 'cause they say you should. Not if they're real friends, that is. 'Cause real friends want you to be happy. And let's face it—life can be pretty groovy when you have a kick-butt boyfriend. So it's time to break out of your comfort zone. Give up a little girl time for some hard-core flirting. Leave the mall a little early—even if you haven't assembled the perfect T-shirt collection yet. It will be so worth it.

Girls and Boys (16–22)

If life were like the Olympics, you'd win a gold medal on the balance beam. Because when it comes to keeping all the things in your life in line, you rule! You don't dis your friends to go hang out with a guy, but you also don't dis guys in the name of being a good friend. You find a way to make video night and hang out with your crush. You talk about more than just your own boy problems. You don't bring your boyfriend along on girls-only activities. You do, however, leave your friends early to go see your crush. And you'll gladly set aside time to spend with your boyfriend. Because you know that both parts of your life are equally important. So we'll just call ya Ms. Sensitive and be on our way. You don't need our advice at all!

Boys, Boys, Boys (23–30)

The female half of the population divides itself into two groups: those who have girlfriends and those who don't. And there is no doubt about which half you fall into. Because you are the classic ditch-your-friends-for-guys chick. As soon as you get a boyfriend, your so-called crew never sees you again. You don't introduce your friends to your BF's single friends, you don't make time to see them unless it's convenient (meaning he has other plans), and you're willing to dismiss their problems at the merest hint of interest from a guy. And that just stinks. 'Cause not only are you missing out on many amazing bonding experiences, you're also almost guaranteeing that you're not going to have any lasting friendships. Your friends aren't going to make an effort to stay in touch when you regularly dis them. Why should they? It's not like you've gone out of your way to be a good friend to them. So what do you do now? Become a good friend, meaning talk to your friends about something other than your boy life. Be a friend. It's as easy as that.

are you a **drama queen?**

Sometimes real-life relationships can be more melodramatic than a soap opera. But you know what? Certain people actually wouldn't want it any other way. They prefer their romances to be chock-full o' intrigue, deceit, and, of course, scenes worthy of a cliff-hanger. Could you be one of those people? Take this quiz and find out! ♥

1. You argue with the guys you go out with:
   a) All the time. About anything. Fighting keeps things interesting.
   b) Once in a while—but only over really important stuff.
   c) Rarely. You like to enjoy the time you spend with the people you date—not waste it bickering.
   d) Never. If you're fighting with a guy, you should be broken up with him already.

2. One of your good girlfriends breaks up with her boyfriend—who you've always had a secret crush on. What do you do?

    a) Wait a few days and then call him up—to console him, of course.

    b) Nothing. He's off-limits.

    c) Call him up immediately and let him know that while you're good friends with what's-her-face, you think he could do better. Then invite him over for a Tomb Raider marathon.

3. The prom's coming up. You've decided to ask the cute guy from your French class. How do you approach him?

    a) Wait till after class, when he's alone, then ask him.

    b) Tell your friends—who are friends with all his friends—that you're thinking about asking him. Before eighth period the whole school will know what's up.

    c) Get on three-way calling with him and your BFF and have her drop hints that you're into him.

4. You heard it through the grapevine that your volleyball teammate's boyfriend has been two-timing her with a chick from your rival school. What do you do?

    a) Run up to her—ASAP—and tell her what you've heard.

    b) Nothing. You're not that tight with her—and besides, you don't even know if the rumors are true.

    c) Keep the grapevine goin'—by telling a few of your friends.

5. The cute guy who works at the Electronics Boutique in the mall thinks that you're his age. You're really three years younger than he is. You:

    a) Admit your age. Lying will just complicate things.

    b) Make plans to go out with him next Saturday. You'll tell Mom you're sleeping over at Sue's house so you don't have to sweat that curfew thing.

    c) Flirt like a maniac! Sure, it may not go anywhere, but you'll always have the food court. Sigh.

6. You and your boyfriend are having a disagreement. At a party. How do you deal?

    a) Agree to wait until later to disagree. After all, nothing's a bigger buzz kill than a nasty love spat at a party!

    b) Find a quiet corner and have it out. You're not gonna make a scene, but if someone does happen to over-hear you two fighting, so be it.

    c) Lock yourself in the bathroom. The line may be long, but the only people you're letting in are your girl-friends—and maybe him, if he's ready to apologize.

7. It's either feast or famine, and after a serious, semester-long dry spell, two guys are sweating you. Bad. What do ya do?

    a) Start dating both of 'em—without telling either of them what's up. Being worshiped is fun!

    b) Talk about it incessantly with your friends. How could you possibly choose between those two babes?

    c) Tell them both about the situation and play 'em off each other. Roses, candy, stuffed animals. Dang! You've never had it so good!

8. Score! Your crush finally came around and asked you out. Only on the big night, you get (gasp!) stood up. How do you deal?

    a) Give him the cold shoulder when you see him in school for the next couple of days. The silent treatment has been known to work miracles!

    b) Tell all your friends about it so they'll think he's a total jerk, too.

    c) Wait to hear his excuse for breaking your date, then go from there. No use in getting all worked up when you don't even know why he left you hangin'.

9. When you broke up with your last BF, what'd you do to deal?

    a) Went out for ice cream with your girl crew.

    b) Listened to Radiohead on repeat every night for a month straight and wallowed in your misery.

    c) Faked sick for two weeks — just so you wouldn't have to see him.

10. Give yourself one point for each of the following you've done:

    a) Dated a friend's ex.

    b) Smooched a guy who had a steady girlfriend.

    c) Started a rumor about someone else to get a guy who was into her to lose interest.

    d) Started a rumor about yourself to get a guy to like you.

    e) Set a friend up with a guy you were so not over.

    f) Ditched out on plans with a guy when a better offer came along.

g) Double booked two dates for the same time.

h) Posed as someone else on-line to get dirt on a guy.

i) Used someone to get to their cute friend.

scoring

1. a-4, b-3, c-2, d-1
2. a-2, b-1, c-3
3. a-1, b-3, c-2
4. a-3, b-1, c-2
5. a-1, b-3, c-2
6. a-1, b-2, c-3
7. a-2, b-1, c-3
8. a-2, b-3, c-1
9. a-1, b-2, c-3
10. Give yourself one point for each.

are you a drama queen?

Drama School Dropout (9–17)

You couldn't care less about drama. The lights, camera, action scene isn't your thing at all. In fact, you're probably a little scared to be center stage. All that attention can be unnerving. Everybody knowing your business, all the intrigue . . . it's all just too much for you to deal with—especially in between social studies homework, field hockey practice, and everything else. And that's fine. Not everyone can be a drama queen. (Thank goodness!) But once in a while you deserve to steal the show—especially if it means standing up for yourself. So by all means, don't let the guy who stood you up off the hook—confront him! Just not in a *Melrose Place* kinda way.

Best Supporting Actress (18–27)

You've been known to cause a commotion every now and again. But you're by no means a true drama diva. For the most part you live through the drama of others—like that girl on your team whose BF is supposedly sneaking around on her. When you do bust out of your supporting role and make a scene, it's usually not the full-on season-finale type of thing. And we can't say that we blame you. Being a drama queen can be draining—and you like to pick and choose your roles.

Drama Queen (28–37)

And the award for best actress in a drama goes to . . . *you!* Yep, sister, you are one class-A drama queen. There's never a dull moment with you around. Just ask your friends and your boyfriend. You totally live for melodrama. Why? Well, to you, things are just plain boring if there isn't some intrigue goin' on. So you scheme, cause scenes, and spread rumors whenever you can. You also make sure that everyone else knows the dirt. After all, what's a little drama without an audience? But as much as your antics amuse everyone around you, they can also get old—fast. So watch your step or you might get kicked out of your place in the spotlight.

is your **crush** crushing back?

There's nothing like a killer crush. Well, except for discovering that the object of said crush is drooling over you, too. So is your sweetie secretly sweating you back? Take this quiz to find out. ♥

1. **Your crush is jamming out to the new Smashmouth CD. When you ask him about it, he:**

    a) Pops it out of his Discman—at lightning speed—and hands it to you.

    b) Says, "Yeah, it's rad. It's different from the last one, but you should definitely check it out."

    c) Tells you it rocks and promises to let you test-drive it after listening to one more track.

2. You most often see your crush . . .

    a) When he's coming around the corner, right after you've just finished your daily snoop in his locker.

    b) After second period when he usually stops by your locker to chat about how wack your math teacher is.

    c) Everywhere. You've got the same social circle, so you see each other all the time.

3. Omigod. By some miracle of fate, you two have been assigned to be each other's lab partners. When it's time to write up your first report, he:

    a) Calls you up and invites you over to work on it together—in the downstairs rec room.

    b) Meets you after school in the library to do it.

    c) Calls up with a lame excuse and sticks you with all the work.

4. Your BFF is moving to France, and you're throwing her a huge going-away party. When you invite your crush, he mentions that coincidentally, his best friend is having a party that same day, adding:

    a) How bummed he'd be if all the hotties chose your party over his friend's.

    b) That he hopes you'll find the time to squeeze in an appearance at his friend's party.

    c) That he'll make sure to stop over at your party on the way to his friend's.

5. The coolest thing about him is:

    a) That mysterious way he has about him.

b) The random stories he tells you whenever you're together.

c) All his weird little quirks—like blushing and tripping over stuff.

6. When he's around you, he mostly talks about:
a) The weather.

b) You.

c) Himself.

7. When you bump into each other at the mall, he usually:
a) Ditches out on his posse at the Sam Goody to schmooze with you and your crew.

b) Mutters a quick, "What's up," before ducking into the nearest store.

c) Looks completely mortified.

8. You're sitting home, watching <u>Roswell</u>, and he calls. It's:
a) To ask you what the math homework is.

b) To ask if you're going to the dorky school dance on Friday.

c) Oops—a wrong number!

9. Does your crush have a girlfriend?
a) Yes.

b) No.

10. Give yourself one point for each of the following your crush has done:
a) Called you.

b) Prank called you.

c) IM-ed you.

d) E-mailed you.

e) Asked one of your friends about you.

f) Come to one of your games/recitals/parties.

g) Been busted full on checking you out.

scoring

1. a-3, b-1, c-2

2. a-1, b-3, c-2

3. a-3, b-2, c-1

4. a-1, b-2, c-3

5. a-1, b-3, c-2

6. a-2, b-3, c-1

7. a-3, b-1, c-2

8. a-2, b-3, c-1

9. a-1, b-2

10. Give yourself one point for each.

is your crush crushing back?

Clueless Crush (9–15)

Hate to break it to you, but according to our findings, you're not even a blip on your crush object's radar. That might mean it's time to get over your current crush and move on. Could be your crush is taken or just isn't interested. But not necessarily. Maybe he just hasn't noticed the wonderfulness that is you. So what are you waiting for? Make him notice! Start a conversation in the halls between classes, bump into him, anything. Just bust a move—and soon—or find someone new to crush on. There are plenty o' hotties out there.

Could Be Crushing (16–27 points)

Hmmm. Your crush object *could* be crushing back. Or not. Our Magic 8 Ball says: "Reply is hazy." Are you just pals—or pals with potential? There's only one way to find out. No, don't ask him outright! That never works! Too much pressure. You've got to play it smart and somewhat safe—so put out your feelers and then go from there. Arrange a group trip to the movies, ask to borrow a CD, whatever. Throw out a line, and see if your crush bites.

Co-Crushing (27–33 points)

Okay, nothing's for certain—not even the fact that Felicity's hair will grow back. But things look really promising for you in the crush department. The signs are all there: You talk, you flirt, you've exchanged longing looks in the cafeteria. You even get a little tongue-tied around each other once in a while. Awww. But while the whole so-does-he-like-me-or-what? routine can be intriguing at first, after a while it gets as stale as yesterday's poppy seed bagel. So stop being so shy, and bust a move to snag that crush, already!

is it time to
break up?

You were crushing on him for, like, *ever*. And then he finally asked you out. Well, you've been boyfriend-girlfriend for a while now, and things are pretty comfy between you two. Maybe too comfy. Maybe so comfy that you can't even tell if you're still into each other anymore. Take this quiz to find out if it's time to break up! ♥

1. The new guy in your science class is doing an impression of a hamster lost in his maze. You're thinking:

    a) "How come Hamster Boy is cuter and funnier than my BF?"

    b) "Hamster Boy is just perfect for my younger sister. They have the same wacky sense of humor, and he'd make the perfect starter boyfriend!"

    c) "Hamster Boy would be pretty cute if he weren't doing that lame hamster thing."

2. You and your BF have Friday night plans to celebrate your six-month anniversary, but your BFF just scored tickets to see *NSYNC. You:

a) Tell your BFF it's a no go. Your sweetie spent too much time planning this evening for you to blow it off at the last minute.

b) Bail on your BF. You can celebrate with him anytime—this is *NSYNC!

c) Tell your BFF you're dying to see the show, but you've gotta check with lover boy first. If skipping his romantic dinner is a biggie, you'd rather miss the concert.

3. You and your BF are watching <u>The Tom Green Show</u>, and he starts cracking up. You:

a) Suddenly realize how annoying his laugh is. God, it's like a Jack Russell terrier.

b. Look over and notice how cute his smile is.

c. Laugh, too. Tom Green is funny!

4. When chatting with guys on-line, how long does it take you to admit that you have a BF?

a) Right away. You don't want those Internet geeks to get any ideas.

b) Not long . . . after they ask.

c) Boyfriend? What boyfriend? Hey, all's fair in love and cyberspace.

5. School ends at three. It's three-thirty. Where is your BF?

a) Shooting hoops with his boys.

b) Hanging out at your house, watching MTV and playing

with your cat.

c) How are you supposed to know?

6. **Your BFF is relaying the day's gossip to you over the phone when your BF calls on the other line. You:**

    a) Tell him you'll call him right back as soon as you hear why Jimbo was suspended and exactly what the gum had to do with it.

    b) Tell your BFF that you'll call her back in a few.

    c) Put them on three-way—your BF will wanna hear this story!

7. **Your BF calls you to say he'll be at your place in twenty minutes. You:**

    a) Take a quick shower, throw on some lip gloss, and park your butt in front of the window so you can see him walking up the driveway.

    b) Take a quick shower, throw on some lip gloss, then search your closet for that skirt he said he likes. You're trying to find the shoes he said were "hot" when the doorbell rings.

    c) Watch the next twenty minutes of *TRL* and open the door in a ponytail and sweats.

8. **He shows up at your doorstep, bringing with him:**

    a) The new Radiohead CD you've been dying to hear.

    b) His favorite movie of all time, *Evil Dead 2,* and two bottles of Mountain Dew. (It's "your" soda.)

    c) That dorky guy he's been hanging around with. You know, the one that calls himself "K Dogg."

9. Your mom refers to your BF:

a) As "your little friend." (e.g., "Where's your little friend today?")

b) As "that dirtbag." (e.g., "You better not bring that dirtbag around the house anymore.")

c) By his birth name. (e.g., Where's Christopher today?")

10. What's you and your BF's smooch sitch?

a) You smooch every time you say hello or good-bye. Including in between classes.

b) About once a week or so, he'll lean over and give you a peck on the cheek.

c) You've been kind of avoiding it since you've started noticing how dry his lips always are.

scoring

1. a-3, b-1, c-2
2. a-1, b-3, c-2
3. a-3, b-1, c-2
4. a-1, b-2, c-3
5. a-2, b-1, c-3
6. a-3, b-1, c-2
7. a-2, b-1, c-3
8. a-1, b-2, c-3
9. a-2, b-3, c-1
10. a-1, b-2, c-3

is it time to break up?

So Happy Together (10–16)

Why are you wasting time with this quiz, girl? Shouldn't you and your BF be staring lovingly into each other's eyes right about now? Neither of you takes the other one for granted, and you express your love to each other by the little things you do plus lots of smooches to carry yourselves through the day. You communicate! And that's why you two are nowhere near the breaking point. Now leave us alone. Your ooey-gooey romance is making our teeth hurt.

Every Rose Has Its Thorns (17–23)

You're sort of at a crossroads here, and your relationship could go either way. Are you two making excuses to avoid each other or to see each other more often? Do you still have stuff to talk about? Try sitting down and making two lists. The first one is called, "Why this relationship is sucking the life out of me." The second one is called, "Why I love and adore my BF more than any other human on earth." If one list ends up being significantly longer than the other one—well—you don't need us to tell you what to do.

You've Lost That Lovin' Feeling (24–30)

Okay, it's over. Done. The time has come to say sayonara to your sweetie 'cause there's really no need for the two of you to keep making each other miserable anymore. Which you are. Not to mention the fact that you're already looking elsewhere. Face it—at this point your middle name is "Wandering Eye." You've even considered Hamster Boy as an option. Doesn't that tell you something? Hamster Boy! Sigh. Give it up. It is so over.

should **YOU** ask him out?

Quick: What's worse, asking a guy out or getting an F on your report card? We're stumped, too. Face it, asking a guy out on a date can be totally nerve-racking. So he'd better be worth the trouble.

So how do you know if you should go for it? Take our quiz. We'll let you know whether you should keep your eyes on this prize or find another sweetie to sweat. ♥

1. **The class president announces a new after-school program placing students in soup kitchens and asks volunteers to raise their hands if they're interested. The guy you're crushing on:**
   a) Signs on immediately.
   b) Mentions that he has to go to softball practice
      instead.
   c) Mentions that he hates soup.

2. You're telling your best, most straight-up, honest friend all about your crush. When she asks, "Yeah, but does he like you back?" You:

  a) Scoff at her question. "Girl, catch a clue. He's only been IM-ing me nonstop since fifth grade!"

  b) Pause for a minute, then say, "Who knows? But he might! So, isn't it worth a shot?"

  c) Realize that you've got no chance. What with the fact that he already has a girlfriend and everything.

3. Not that you were checking up on him or anything, but you have been keeping close tabs on his flirting behavior around school lately. How would you describe it?

  a) Like the Lauryn Hill song from a couple of years back: "[He] can't take his eyes off of you."

  b) Sure, he's flirting with every girl in sight. But hey, that includes you, right?

  c) How do you spell D-O-G?

4. Manners matter. How does this guy measure up?

  a) He's a true-blue nice guy. A real chair-puller-outer. 'Nuff said.

  b) He means well, even if he forgets to say "thanks" when you buy him a Coke.

  c) Is belching considered polite in this country?

5. Head trip alert: Fast-forward to the day when you finally introduce him to your dad. What does Dad have to say to your new beau?

  a) "I'm glad to meet you. You seem like a nice guy.

Would you like to golf together on Sunday?"

b) "Wear your seat belts, and be back here by ten. I'll wait up."

c) "What's that smell?"

6. You see him at the bookstore browsing through the magazine section. Thinking quickly, you stake out a spot by the cash register so you can see what he actually buys. His selection?

a) *Spin*. (How cool is that?)

b) *People*. (Well, we all have a guilty pleasure or two.)

c) *World Wildlife Wrestling Monthly*. (No comment.)

7. A survey says that boys with good grades make better boyfriends. So you decide to sneak a peek at his report card. How's he doing?

a) Well, not everyone can be college material, after all.

b) Hello, Mr. Honor Roll, National Merit Scholar, valedictorian to be.

c) So he's falling a little behind in chemistry. Who isn't? Besides, his English grades are nearly perfect.

8. Last time you tried to flirt with him, he responded with:

a) "Hey, how'd you do on that biology test?"

b) "You are so beautiful, I don't know what to say!"

c) "Hi. Um, what's your name again?"

9. Give his worthiness an extra point for each of the following your crush can call his own (check all that apply):

a) Regular haircuts.

b) A best friend with a steady girlfriend.

c) More than one sister.

d) Perfect school attendance.

e) A phat CD collection that includes plenty of classics, not just new stuff.

f) Floss.

g) A cell phone, with his mom's number on speed dial.

scoring

1. a-3, b-2, c-1

2. a-3, b-2, c-1

3. a-3, b-2, c-1

4. a-3, b-2, c-1

5. a-3, b-2, c-1

6. a-3, b-2, c-1

7. a-1, b-3, c-2

8. a-2, b-3, c-1

9. Give yourself one point for each.

should you ask him out?

Not Now and Maybe Never (8–14)

It might be smart to let this one sit for a while. . . . It sounds like he needs some serious schooling—in life and how the world works—before he's really ready for his prime-time dating debut. Maybe he's a player, maybe he's a freak, maybe he's a straight-up loser, or maybe he's just a little lost and immature, but the fact is, he rates low on the crush-worthiness scale. Look elsewhere—there are far better crushes to be had.

Worth a Shot (15–21)

Okay, so maybe he's not exactly Freddie Prinze, Jr., but hey, who is? (Probably not even F. P. J., but that's another story.) This guy might just have enough pluses to make it worth your while to get to know him a little better. And there's always a chance that some of his minuses might be forgivable or even cute. You know, like those tube socks he wears every day. Awww.

Mr. Perfect (22–31)

What, exactly, are you waiting for? This dude not only looks awesome on paper, he looks pretty good in real life! And get this: Chances are, he'll say "yes." Get yourself together and get in his face, already—it's time the two of you start chilling together. Just remember that no one is truly totally perfect, so if he does eventually show a flaw or two, take it easy on him. Keep your expectations realistic.

are you honest with your BF?

Okay, so there's no rule that says you have to spill every little thing to your sweetie. It's not like you guys have to do a mind meld just 'cause you're going out. But there is a difference between not mentioning some details 'cause they're not important and being a shady lady. Take this quiz to find out if you're honest with your boo. ♥

1. Your BF wants to go in-line skating again, but your shins are still purple from your last roller escapades. Needless to say, you're so not up for it. You say:

    a) "I'm still a little sore from last time. Let's do something else, puh-leez!"

    b) "You think I'm gonna let you maul me like last time? Nuh-uh, buddy."

    c) "Sure! Lemme just grab my shin guards."

2. You're spilling the deets to your BFF about the big fight you and your sweetie had last night when he walks up and asks what you're talking about. You say:

a) "Nothing, honey," and plant a smooch on him to divert attention.

b) "Girl stuff," and give him a look that says you were talking about stuff he really wouldn't wanna hear about.

c) "I was telling her what a jerk you were last night," and then give him a dirty look to let him know you're still feelin' a little salty.

3. Would you ever check your e-mail in front of your BF?

a) Not that it's any of his business, but yeah, why not? You don't have anything to hide.

b) Are you kidding? Like he really needs to see all the pics you're trading with guys from your blink-182 mailing list.

c) No way! If he saw the love letters that the Aussie guy you met in a chat room was sending you, he'd freak!

4. He wants you to go out to dinner with his fam, but you don't think you can stand sitting through another meal while his little bro smears his entrée all over his face (didn't they teach him how to chew?). You tell him:

a) You'd rather eat gum off the floor than go to a restaurant with his family. And that they should get his brother a muzzle.

b) That you'd love to, but you already made dinner plans.

c) That you can't go because your grandmother swal-
lowed a chopstick in a freak Chinese food accident and
you have to visit her in the hospital.

5. **When you tell him you're out with the girls, you're really:**
a) Out with the girls. Like you said. Duh!
b) Out with that cute guy from chorus.
c) Out with the girls and that cute guy from chorus.
What? It's not like you're lying.

6. **Your BF's roaming eye is really getting on your nerves
lately. It seems like he's always checking out other girls! You
deal by:**
a) Complaining to everyone but him about what an
insensitive jerk he is.
b) Telling him (in a one-on-one convo) to please knock it
off 'cause it makes you feel horrible.
c) Waiting till you catch him scoping someone out, then
yelling, "Ugh, you like her? You can have her! I'm
through with this! I can't stand you!" and storming off.

7. **Your BF's oral report is due tomorrow. When he does a
practice run for you, you're horrified to find that he's written
a rap about Abe Lincoln. You:**
a) Try to steer him away from his rap idea. Tell him that
while it's very creative, you don't think the rest of the
class will "get it."
b) Tell him that it's great and maybe he should write a
more traditional intro to his rap so his teacher doesn't
get too freaked out. You'll help him, of course!

c) Spend the next twenty minutes hysterically laughing. "Abraham was born in a log cabin / and when it came to slavery, he wasn't havin' it!" Come on! That doesn't even rhyme!

8. Your BF asks how many guys you've kissed before him. You:

a) Avoid giving him a number by saying things like, "Only one who counts!" or, "A lady never kisses and tells!"

b) Tell him you've only kissed three guys, no matter how many you actually have. Your first kiss, your ex, and him.

c) Give him the score but make sure he fesses up, too.

9. You're chatting with your on-line cyberfriend (who's a guy) when your BF comes into the room. You:

a) Get rid of the IM and sign off right away. You don't know what incriminating evidence could be on there.

b) Ask him to type hello to your friend—you've already told your BF all about him, anyway.

c) Tell your friend you gotta go and log off.

10. Your BF asks what you think of the pic of himself he selected to use for his column in the school newspaper. You think he looks like a total dork. You tell him:

a) That it's the worst pic you've ever seen, and if he actually looked like that, you'd never have dated him in the first place.

b) That he looks cute—but there's another pic where he looks really hot, and maybe he should use that one.

c) That it's a great shot, and you love it. Then call your BFF and start cracking up. Tell her she better pick up the next issue 'cause he's gonna have the most heinous photo in it.

scoring

1. a-2, b-1, c-3
2. a-2, b-3, c-1
3. a-1, b-2, c-3
4. a-1, b-2, c-3
5. a-1, b-3, c-2
6. a-3, b-1, c-2
7. a-2, b-3, c-1
8. a-2, b-3, c-1
9. a-3, b-1, c-2
10. a-1, b-2, c-3

are you honest with your BF?

The Truth, the Whole Truth, and Nothing but the Truth (10–16)

When it comes to truth tellin', you don't fool around. As a matter of fact, you're brutally honest. Emphasis on brutal. Yowch! You're certainly not hiding anything from your honey, but you've probably reduced him to tears once or twice. Hey, honesty is great. It helps him trust you. It brings you closer. But here's a shocker: Sometimes a little white lie isn't so bad. We commend your ability to be so straight up, but maybe you should soften the blow sometimes, okay?

White Lie Woman (17–23)

Okay, so you don't tell your BF *everything*, but who says he needs to know every little thing you say and do? You need a little bit of privacy, and that's all right. In fact, it's probably best if you don't tell him that you think his face looks like a pizza in his yearbook photo. What's not cool is telling him you're hanging with your girls when you're on a date with Señor Hottie from Spanish class. Just make sure that the stuff you keep to yourself isn't stuff that could harm your relationship and that the lies you do tell are of the "little white" variety.

Secrets and Lies (24–30)

If you put half the creativity that you use to concoct elaborate stories to feed your boyfriend into writing a novel, you could be the next Anne Rice. Listen, you deserve privacy as much as the next girl, but your BF also deserves a little respect. Little white lies are one thing, but if you can't be straight with him about things like whether you've got another on-line BF or that you're dating another hombre on the sly, maybe you should rethink your relationship.

are you into the
wrong guys?

There are all kinds of guys out there—but some of 'em are boyfriend material and some of 'em are, well, not. Do you go after the guys who'll give you what you need—or the ones who'll give you grief? Take this quiz, and find out for sure!

1. Is bad good?

a) Yep. The badder, the better!

b) Nope. They're trouble.

c) Depends on what your definition of "bad" is.

2. Would you date a guy who's a friend?

a) Heck, yeah! If a guy's a good bud, that ups his chances of being a good boyfriend.

b) Not even! That'd be like kissing your brother.

c) Depends on the guy. Duh!

3. Have you ever crushed on someone from afar—who you didn't really know?

a) Yep. All the time!

b) Nope.

c) No—that's not crushing. That's infatuation.

4. How long did your most serious relationship last?

a) A few days. It was totally intense, but very short-lived. Kinda like a volcanic eruption.

b) A few weeks. Then you both figured out it wasn't going anywhere.

c) A few months. You had some good times, but it wasn't working out, so you moved on.

d) Six months or longer. You guys went through a lot together, and you're still cool with each other.

e) Relationship? Yeah, right! Does your crush on Paul Walker count?

5. There's a big dance coming up. Everyone's going. Your crush:

a) Might ask you. Or might get his best friend to ask your best friend to ask you.

b) Might go with you—if you told him it was, like, your dying wish.

c) Will most likely go solo and then hang with his boy crew *the whole night*.

d) Would probably go with you—if either of you had the nerve to pop the question.

e) Wouldn't be caught dead at a school dance.

6. What usually starts you crushin' on someone?
a) You figure out you have mutual interests—like you're both a little too into WWF and the Beastie Boys.
b) Looks, social status, the way he dresses . . . you know, the deep stuff.
c) It's all about cool conversations. 'Nuff said?
d) That feeling in the pit of your stomach when you see him. Like you wanna hurl.
e) An inexplicable mixture of friendship and attraction.

7. What type of guys totally turn you off?
a) Guys with no social skills.
b) Guys you're too good friends with.
c) Poseurs.
d) Guys who always act immature.
e) Unpopular guys. You know—drama geeks, nerds, guys who don't like sports, etc.
f) Guys who are too nice.

8. Your BFF's boyfriend breaks up with her. Is he fair game?
a) Yeah—all's fair in love and war.
b) No way, no day. Dating a friend's ex—isn't that like breaking one of the Ten Commandments?
c) Sure—but who'd want to date some dude who was dumb enough to dump your friend?

9. Your current crush (check all that apply):
a) Just broke up with someone.

b) Has a girlfriend.

c) Cheated on the last person he dated.

d) Has dated everyone in your grade.

e) Has dated your best friend.

f) Is five years older than you.

g) Doesn't know your name.

scoring

1. a-3, b-1, c-2
2. a-1, b-3, c-2
3. a-3, b-2, c-1
4. a-4, b-3, c-2, d-1, e-5
5. a-2, b-4, c-3, d-1, e-5
6. a-2, b-5, c-3, d-4, e-1
7. a-3, b-4, c-1, d-2, e-5, f-5
8. a-3, b-2, c-1
9. Give yourself one point for each

are you into the wrong guys?

Right On (7–15 points)

Congrats! You go for the right kinds of guys. Well, as "right" as anyone can go for, anyway. 'Cause hooking up with a hottie is complicated stuff for sure. Even if a guy's cool, cute, and considerate, that doesn't mean you're guaranteed boy bliss—there's a ton of other issues that come up during the dating game. Just 'cause someone's a nice guy doesn't mean that he's boyfriend material. But it does mean that his heartbreak factor is substantially lower. And lucky for you, you're upping your odds of getting together with a great guy—because you use your head and not just your heart. You know that looks aren't everything. You know that friendship and mutual respect are more valuable qualities to have in a relationship than butterflies in the pit of your stomach.

Once Bitten, but Not Shy (16–25 points)

Okay, so you've had a little bad luck with boys. But just 'cause you've been burned once or twice doesn't necessarily mean that you go for guys who are total bad news. The truth is that sometimes it's kinda hard to pick a bad seed outta the bunch. It's not like you can tell just by looking at a guy whether he's crush worthy or not. So how do you guarantee that you're spared the heartache and pain of going out with a loser boy? You can't. Well, not, like, completely, anyway. But there are things you can do to up your chances of getting together with a great guy. Like becoming friends with someone before getting all romantic and giving nice guys (or even guys you think you wouldn't want to go out with in a zillion years) a shot. And avoiding guys who've dated your friends—or half the school—like the plague. 'Cause scammers don't change.

Big Trouble (26–35 points)

Whoa, girl! According to our calculations, you've been going for the wrong guys. What do we mean by this? Well, every bad boy magnet is different—but chances are that you're into scammers, guys who don't know what they want, or guys who just aren't interested in you. Or maybe your problem is that you just don't give certain guys a chance—because they're either your friends or they're "too nice." As a result, your experiences with dating have most likely been a bit on the traumatic side. We're talking about unreturned phone calls, severely messy breakups, etc. So how do you change all this? Be more open to other kinds of guys—not just the kind that make you feel like you wanna puke when you talk to 'em. 'Cause that's not a good sign.

are you in love?

Sure, your stomach does that flip-flop thing when you kiss. And yeah, you laugh till your cheeks hurt when the two of you hang out. But does that mean it's love—or merely a hard-core crush? After all, there's more to L-O-V-E than Friday night dates to the movies and passing notes in study hall. Take this quiz and find out! ♥

1. **He's stuck at home with that nasty flu he caught from his little brother, and he looks so ill, he makes Seth Green from <u>Idle Hands</u> look like he's ready to run the marathon. When you stop by to visit, you:**

    a) Kiss him full on the lips—germs be damned! And look how sweet you are, you even brought echinacea.

    b) Are shocked to see what a difference a couple of missed showers can make in his appearance. You start to feel a little ill yourself.

c) Um, does that one phone call count as stopping by?

2. Yay, you! You just found out that you've made the honor roll. Naturally, the first person you want to share the good news with is:

   a) Your mom. She'll be so proud.
   b) Your boyfriend. He loves to brag about what a brainiac you are.
   c) Your English teacher. Ha! And she accused you of slacking off lately.

3. After four months of relationship bliss, you and the boy finally have your first major blowout (he ditched you last minute to go to the batting range with his boys). How do you resolve it?

   a) Give each other the silent treatment for a week. Whoever breaks down first will be the winner of this round.
   b) Discuss it rationally. Okay, first you get salty and throw out a few good one-liners, but then you make up and seal it with a kiss.
   c) Brood for three days and let it blow over. Whatever.

4. You just spotted him and a Christina Aguilera look-alike (ugh—wearing a supershort field hockey uniform, no less) talking in the hallway. She even had the nerve to tug on his wallet chain! Automatically you assume:

   a) He's cheating on you.
   b) He's attracted to her. Maybe.
   c) Nothing. Okay, you're a tad jealous, but he's your BF—not hers. Besides, you trust him.

5. True or false: You both have really deep, dark, incriminating secrets that you've shared with each other:

   a) True.

   b) False.

   c) True. And it took three days before you'd even hold hands again. *Ew.*

6. You promised him that you'd hang out while he baby-sits his bratty nephew Friday night. Only turns out that the big Get Fired Up homecoming pep rally is the same evening. You:

   a) Deal. After all, the two of you could have fun doing anything—even playing Chutes and Ladders with a whiny five-year-old.

   b) Keep your promise, but spend the entire time wishing you were huddled around the bonfire with your buds, drinking hot chocolate.

   c) Ditch him. He can't expect you to play Romper Room on the biggest night of the year.

7. Uh-oh. You got back your history midterm—with a big, fat D scrawled at the top. You feel like crying. When he sees the look on your face, he:

   a) Knows immediately that something's up and passes you a note: "Are you okay? Let's meet at our spot after class."

   b) Gives you the usual nod, then commences hurling occasional spitballs at you.

   c) Continues scribbling in his notebook. If you want to talk about something, *you'll* bring it up.

8. You've fantasized about being picked to be a cast member for the new <u>Real World—Rio</u>! Sun, phat digs, and hot roomies. But when you get to the part in the fantasy about leaving your BF for six months, you realize that in real life you would:

a) Pull a Pam and be true to your sweetie. Okay, so she started dating Judd after vacating the house, but still, she never cheated during the real run!

b) Go Flora all the way: Keep your man, but cheat on him on the sly. What he doesn't know won't hurt him.

c) Try to resist temptation à la Danny but succumb while partying during Carnival. Oops.

9. Give yourself one point for each of the following "true" statements:

a) You can tell each other anything, even embarrassing stuff like how you once peed your pants in first grade.

b) Even though you disagree, you respect each other's opinions (e.g., he thinks WWF rules; you think it's the lowest form of entertainment today).

c) You can have a giant undergrounder zit on your nose and garlic breath and he'd still wanna smooch.

d) You have at least four private jokes that no one else would get.

e) You'd do something you hate just because he's into it and vice versa.

f) He's acted like a total fool in public, and you're still attracted to him.

g) You both remember major milestones in your relationship, like the date of your first kiss (heck, you even remember the song that was playing in the background).

h) You've had at least one fight that brought you both to tears but worked it out.

10. **Your former crush—the one who dissed you so publicly, he might as well have done it over the loudspeaker during morning announcements so the entire school was privy to your humiliation—is sweatin' you bad. Word is, he'd do anything to get you to go out with him. Are you tempted?**

a) Maybe. The dude's got it goin' on. You owe it to yourself to see if there's still a spark, right?

b) No way. Sure, it'd be kinda cool to make him grovel, but you're completely content with your current man.

c) Er, let's just say you've already taken a bite of the forbidden apple.

scoring

1. a-3, b-2, c-1

2. a-2, b-3, c-1

3. a-1, b-3, c-2

4. a-1, b-2, c-3

5. a-3, b-1, c-2

6. a-3, b-2, c-1

7. a-3, b-2, c-1

8. a-3, b-1, c-2

9. Give yourself one point for each.

10. a-2, b-3, c-1

are you in love?

What's Love Got to Do with It? (10–15)

Hate to break it to you, but it doesn't look like you've got a
love connection. Sure, you're attracted to each other and
like hanging out, but as for L-O-V-E? It doesn't look like it's
in the cards for you. Could be you're just not ready for a
real commitment. Or perhaps you don't feel completely
comfortable with each other. Whatever it is, the necessary
ingredients aren't there. And that's cool—it'll happen sooner
or later with the *right* person. And when it does, you'll
know it.

Crush Groove (16–24)

Things are good in Relationship Land. Really good, even.
Still, it ain't love—at least, not yet. No matter how much
the two of you like each other, not all relationships turn into
true love. On the other hand, maybe the two of you just
haven't been together long enough, or maybe you're taking
it slow. How do you know for sure? Well, it's a tough call—
Cupid's not going to send you a memo or anything alerting
you that today's *the day*, but when it happens, you just
know. So, stick it out and see what happens. In the mean-
time enjoy what you have. Even if it doesn't turn out to be
everlasting love, it sounds pretty sweet.

Endless Love (25–35)

It's official—you are undoubtedly, unabashedly, blissfully in
love. Er, scratch the blissful part. 'Cause you see, you know

that being really in love isn't all Godiva chocolates and roses. It's also about compromise, trust, sharing, understanding—and all the zits that come with it. For example, yeah, you get a twinge of jealousy when you see the class flirt throwing her mojo at your BF. But you trust him and are secure enough in your relationship to know that nothing shady's going down. And most important, you can talk about anything—even mortifying stuff—and know that you're still on for Sadie Hawkins. Prepare to get voted Cutest Couple for the yearbook!

are you a good date?

Yeah, yeah, you've got it goin' on and all. You're busy every night of the week. But how good are you at this dating thing, really? If you want to be a good date, part of the job description is making sure that he's having a good time, too. How do you rate as a date? Take this quiz. ♥

1. Your crush asks you out for Saturday night with a, "What do you want to do?" Your answer:

a) "Arcade games and a movie. Up for it?"

b) "Well, from seven to seven forty-five we'll eat a well-balanced meal. We'll see an eight o'clock movie, then make out for five minutes. You'll take me home and drop me off at exactly ten-ten. Okay?"

c) "Oh, I don't care; whatever you want to do."

2. Score! You've been asked out. You:

a) Race to tell your ex-crush (the one who obviously didn't know a good thing when it was standing right in front of his face).

b) Discuss it at lunch with anyone who will listen.

c) Tell just your best friend—hey, you need a little support!

3. You're meeting your date in one hour. You:

a) Hop in the shower and start getting ready.

b) Continue chatting on-line—who cares if you smell a little?

c) Have already been grooming and working on your outfit all day.

4. You meet at the movie theater. You say:

a) "Nice shoes. Let's go in."

b) "Wow, you look great!"

c) "You're wearing that?"

5. You're at dinner. You order:

a) A side salad and ice water.

b) Whatever your date orders.

c) Whatever you're in the mood for.

6. What do you and your date talk about at dinner?

a) Schoolwork.

b) Your problems.

c) Stuff you know you have in common.

7. How many times do you hit the bathroom during dinner?

a) Only when you need to.

b) At least once, no matter what.

c) Enough to make your date really wonder what you're doing in there.

8. Check, please! Here comes the bill. You:

a) Reach for it, saying, "This one's on me. Your turn next time around!"

b) Suggest you split the tab.

c) Head for the bathroom again.

9. Your date buys the movie tickets. You:

a) Say, "Thanks!"

b) Offer to spring for popcorn.

c) Grab your ticket and head for the seats.

10. During the movie, you:

a) Talk incessantly.

b) Fall asleep.

c) Hold hands, if you feel like it.

11. Date's over. You expect:

a) At least a kiss good night, so no matter how you feel about him, you pucker up.

b) Him to thank you for the privilege of your company.

c) Nothing. But if there's a kiss in the works, score!

12. The next day you:

a) Call to see if you're both into it and plan a repeat.

b) Get a friend to find out what your date has to say about it.

c) Do nothing. If he wants to go out again, he can ask you.

scoring

1. a-3, b-2, c-1
2. a-1, b-2, c-3
3. a-3, b-1, c-2
4. a-2, b-3, c-1
5. a-1, b-2, c-3
6. a-2, b-1, c-3
7. a-3, b-2, c-1
8. a-3, b-2, c-1
9. a-2, b-3, c-1
10. a-1, b-2, c-3
11. a-2, b-1, c-3
12. a-3, b-2, c-1

are you a good date?

Dud Date (12–19)

You're bored, uninterested, and not very thoughtful. You believe that your date should be thankful for the opportunity to go out with you and that he should take care of all the planning and paying. Girl, you need to give a little more of your divine self!

Ask the poor guy some questions about his life—at best you'll find out that there's more to him than meets the eye; at worst, you'll make the time go by faster.

Decent Date (20–29)

You're cool to hang with and generally fun to have around. But when it comes to the actual date, your behavior is a little off track. Maybe you're a little insecure about the whole dating scene? Don't worry about it. Odds are—your date's just as freaked as you.

Dream Date! (30–36)

You've got lots to offer—fun conversation, cool ideas for where to go, a winning personality. You don't put any pressures on your date—instead you're as chill and easygoing as they come. Not to mention funny and smart, and maybe even a good kisser. Bet you're busy this weekend.

are you too needy?

Do you need your ego stroked all the time? Or do you know how great you are without anyone else having to tell you? Take this quiz to determine your neediness quotient. ♥

1. Your best friend has just flipped for her new dude. They've been spending, like, every single second together for the past three weeks. You find this:

    a) Slightly annoying—after all, she's the one who's
       always blabbing about how she would never pick a
       boy over her friends. Yeah, right!

    b) Completely nauseating (gag!)—and grounds for a
       serious verbal smackdown from you. After all, you
       need a BFF who's gonna represent!

c) Natural—everyone spends a lot of time with their new boo at first.

2. **You're at a party when the school flirt starts shamelessly eyeballing your guy. You:**
   a) Grab hold of his arm while shooting her dirty looks. That should make her back off!
   b) Couldn't care less. You know your BF's gonna be kissing you good night later—not her.
   c) Tell your guy you're not feeling well and go into the other room. If he knows what's good for him, he'll come running after you immediately!

3. **You like it best when a guy calls you:**
   a) Every single day. And an IM or two wouldn't hurt, either.
   b) Every couple of days. Anything more than that and the conversation is in danger of getting lame.
   c) Whenever you guys have something to talk about.

4. **You've been totally dying to see the new Will Smith flick. But none of your friends will go with you. You decide to:**
   a) Go alone. Yeah, you'd rather not go by yourself—but it's not that big of a deal.
   b) Call your BFF and plead with her to go. You'll even pay her way!
   c) Get your little sis to go with you. She may not be your ideal movie date, but hey, going with a sib is better than going solo!

5. It's the first day of school, and you realize that none of your friends have lunch the same period as you. What do you do?

   a) Suck it up and try to hook up with a new chat-'n'-chew crew.

   b) See your guidance counselor and get her to let you drop a class or two so you end up with the exact same schedule as your BFF.

   c) Take advantage of your extra time by eating lunch in study hall. Anything to avoid being spotted in the caf without your posse.

6. You've been waiting for your BFF to pick you up for almost an hour. What do you do?

   a) You head for her place and plan on bawling her out big time when you get there. How dare she keep you waiting!

   b) Feel a little peeved but decide to wait and talk to your friend before wigging out.

   c) Wonder if she's okay. After all, it is so unlike her to flake on you. Maybe something's wrong.

7. It's 8 P.M. on a Friday. Most likely, you're:

   a) Frantically trying to round up your friends for a movie night, a party, whatever. Staying in is so not an option.

   b) Waiting to hear what's going on from your crew. You're not desperate to go out—the weekend is young, after all—but if something's up, you're game.

   c) Really beat. You're not leaving your spot on the sofa unless something major is happening.

8. You like it when the guys you go out with:

a) Shower you with compliments.

b) Fawn over you—constantly.

c) Base their schedules on yours.

d) Put you above everyone else.

e) None of the above.

f) All of the above.

9. You have a boyfriend:

a) All the time. Being single is for losers!

b) More often than not. You're a total fox, after all.

c) Hardly ever. But you really, really want one.

d) Once in a while. But you're more concerned about quality than quantity.

e) Never. But when the right guy comes along, who knows what will happen?

10. If your phone hasn't rung for an hour or two, you:

a) Pick up the phone and call your BFF just to "check in."

b) Call the phone company and ask them to check if there's trouble on your line.

c) Find that you enjoy the peace and quiet.

scoring

1. a-2, b-3, c-1

2. a-2, b-1, c-3

3. a-3, b-2, c-1

4. a-1, b-3, c-2

5. a-1, b-3, c-2

6. a-3, b-2, c-1
7. a-3, b-2, c-1
8. a-2, b-3, c-5, d-4, e-1, f-6
9. a-3, b-2, c-3, d-1, e-0,
10. a-2, b-3, c-1

are you too needy?

Needy? Not Even! (10–14)

You, needy? Puh-lease. You couldn't care less about being
validated by others—'cause you rely on yourself for that.
Which means that you have no problem doing things on
your own. You don't mind hitting the multiplex without your
crew—heck, every now and then you might even prefer
going solo. You realize the value of being able to do stuff
on your own. But it's not like you're a loner, either. You
have plenty of friends—maybe even a boyfriend. You're just
not the kinda girl who needs to be reassured by 'em all the
time. In fact, you probably think the type of guys who are
constantly sweating their girls are, well, annoying. And
that's cool and all, but let's face it—everybody needs somebody once in a while. Just don't be too strong or too proud
to show it when you do.

Kinda Clingy (15–23)

Okay, so you're not desperately needy. But you definitely
do have some needy tendencies. Which means that while
you can be totally confident and self-sufficient a lot of the
time, you've been known, on occasion, to turn into one of

those clingy chicks. You may hate to be alone. Or could be
that you need your guy to prove just how into you he is—
like, all the time. Or maybe you just get a little jealous
when some girl starts hitting on your guy. Whatever sets
you off, don't beat yourself up about it. After all, everyone
feels a pang of neediness now and again. It's totally natural.
Just don't let it get too outta hand. 'Cause while it's cool to
show your vulnerability once in a while, there is no bigger
buzz kill than a total cling-on. But you knew that.

Needy and Greedy (24–35)

Uh-oh. Looks like you are seriously needy. You require con-
stant coddling from your friends and from guys, too. If
you're not hanging out with them, getting called by 'em, or
just generally being sweated by 'em, you feel seriously neg-
lected. And while it's true that everyone loves attention,
there's a big difference between liking it and living for it.
Lesson number one: Learn to rely less on others—and more
on yourself—to feel good. That means not needing to be
reassured all the time. If you're kicking it on the couch
alone on a Friday night, it's not the end of the world. And
you're not a total loser.

are you
obsessed with
your crush?

So you've memorized your crush's schedule and you ride your bike past his house so often his mother's starting to suspect something. Does this mean that you're very thorough or that you're completely obsessed? Take this quiz and find out! ♥

1. It's the first day of school. You walk into your new home-room and immediately spot the guy you had a crush on all last year. (Hey, is that the "Hallelujah Chorus" playing in your head?) You:

    a) Slide into the seat behind him. When you're sure his attention is focused on exchanging summer stories with his friends, you steal a long, hard look at his schedule and write it down. From now on wherever he goes, you'll be waiting!

b) Square your shoulders and take the seat next to him. When he inevitably turns your way, smile and say, "Hey, weren't you in Mr. Johnson's class last year?

c) Head over to where your friend is sitting across the room. Can you say prime staring location?

2. It's the first night of the annual youth hiking trip your mom always forces you to go on, and for once, you're not completely miserable. Oh, you're freezing cold and have oozing blisters, as always. But this year a Ryan Phillippe look-alike has joined the trip, and he just lent you his sweatshirt! You:

a) Thank him profusely, wear it the entire trip (which you spend talking to him, natch), then return it when you get back to base camp. You've never been so sorry to leave the woods behind.

b) Wear it the night he offers it to you, put it in your bag, and "forget" about it for the rest of the trip. When you get home, you pull it out immediately and show it to all your friends, then stash it under your pillow. He'll be the last thing you smell before you fall asleep and the first thing you're aware of when you wake up in the morning.

c) Wear it the whole trip, but neglect to give it to him in the rush of saying good-bye and exchanging info. Wait four days, then call him to say you have his hoodie and want to return it.

3. You're digging through your locker for your vocabulary list when you hear your third-period crush giving his e-mail password to a friend. You:

a) Banish his password to your mental trash can. Your knowledge of vocabulary needs some company, anyway.

b) Shut your locker loudly, stick your head around the corner, and say, "Yo, I heard that." If he doesn't change it in the next twelve hours, his e-mail is fair game.

c) Stand silently until you're sure he's gone, then write it down so you won't forget. Then hack into his e-mail as soon as you get home. It may be wrong, but it is so worth it!

4. **It's Saturday night. You're stuck baby-sitting a sleeping toddler while everyone else is out partying. How do you entertain yourself?**

a) Watch TV. Dude, they have every pay cable channel and then some. Besides, that babe from your fourth-period history class has his own public access show. Two full hours of uninterrupted staring. It's almost better than a party!

b) Do your homework. If you can't party with your crew, you might as well be as productive as possible.

c) Call your crush on the phone, listen to the message, then hang up. Repeat the process every ten minutes till someone comes home. You could listen to his voice forever!

5. **How did you get over the last guy who rejected you?**

a) Dug up all the dirt you could on your ex, published it on your home page, and waited for everyone to realize that he is, in fact, a big, fat loser.

b) Called him every hour, demanding an explanation.

When he finally turned his ringer off, you vented by writing a long, deeply felt poem about how much he smells, which you read at your school's annual poetry slam. Only by that point you realized you were still in love with him, so you started calling him and saying you forgave him and wanted to get back together again.

c) Sold all the CDs you had ever borrowed from him, blacked out his face in the photo booth shots you took together, and kissed a random guy the very next weekend.

d) Cried in your room all weekend while listening to "I Will Remember You" on repeat. Whenever you weren't sobbing incoherently to a friend or eating pints of chocolate ice cream, that is.

6. Your fellow prom committee members decided to sell candygrams to raise money, and you've totally avoided doing your share. Now you've got one week left and fifty candygrams to sell. Looks like you're gonna have to buy some—okay, most of 'em—yourself. Who do you give your candy to?

a) Yourself. If you have to give up hope of that red pleather skirt, you deserve some kind of reward.

b) Everyone you happen to run into until they're gone. You know, your lab partner, your best friend, her hot older brother. . . .

c) Your crush, pretending they're from an anonymous other person, of course. As long as you get to deliver 'em yourself, you wouldn't care if they all melted inside your new backpack!

7. Which <u>Dawson's</u> character has a love life most like yours?

 a) Pacey.

 b) Dawson.

 c) Joey.

 d) Jen.

 e) Henry.

 f) Andie.

 g) Jack.

8. What kind of info have you gathered about your crush? (Don't lie.)

 a) All his favorites: color, food, car, *Friends* character, class . . .

 b) All the above plus random tidbits: middle name, blood type, class schedule, *Crazy Taxi* high score, preferred underwear type . . .

 c) You don't know—whatever he's told you about himself in conversation, you guess.

9. At some point in the past you have (give yourself one point for each):

 a) Waited in a hallway for a guy to walk by.

 b) Told lies about your crush's GF so they'd break up.

 c) Become friends with someone so you could pump him for info about someone else.

 d) Broken into your crush's locker.

 e) Purposely dropped something so a guy would pick it up and talk to you.

 f) Climbed through somebody's window without being invited first.

g) Made friends with your crush's family in order to get closer to him.

h) Spied on a guy through his window.

i) Joined an extracurricular just because of who was in it.

scoring

1. a-3, b-1, c-2,
2. a-1, b-3, c-2
3. a-1, b-2, c-3
4. a-2, b-1, c-3
5. a-2, b-3, c-2, d-1
6. a-1, b-2, c-3
7. a-3, b-2, c-1, d-1, e-4, f-2, g-2
8. a-2, b-3, c-1
9. Give yourself one point for each.

are you obsessed with your crush?

So Not Obsessed (9–15)

Not only are you not the obsessive type, you barely even know how to flirt. And that is just not good. Unless, of course, you want all your crushes to remain just that . . . crushes. But if you want one of them to become something more, you have got to channel the little schemer inside all of us. Which just means you should recognize opportunities and use them! You have some extra candygrams to give away, give at least one to someone special. You overhear a hot guy's e-mail password? Don't forget it—tell him to change it, or send him an e-mail, or do something that will initiate actual contact. Guys are not mind readers. They don't know you like them just because you think about them all day long. And they don't like taking risks any more than you do. That's what flirting is for—to test and see if people like you back. So get up, get out, and get a move on. Too many people still have no idea how awesome you are!

Slightly Obsessed (16–22)

Nobody would ever call you Ms. Innocent. But we can't really say you've crossed the line, either. You're just . . . street-smart. And we sooo dig it. Like, you notice when your crush is around and you use those opportunities to seek him out, but you so don't go overboard. And you wouldn't steal a guy's class schedule, but you're not above arranging to be in the right time and right place to have lunch with him, either. After all, a shared obsession with Gorditas can turn into something more! So go on with your bad self. As you know, if you want something in life, you have to go after it (or him). But you also can't let that thing consume you. And you don't. You rock!

Severely Obsessed (23–33)

We are afraid. Very, very afraid. But not as afraid as the objects of your obsession must be. It's time to stop. Right now, before you scare the living daylights out of the poor guy. Luckily, stopping is possible. All you have to do is start to recognize the difference between what is normal crush behavior and what is out of hand. Here's a quick guide: Choosing a locker because it's near your crush, normal; following someone home and watching him through his bedroom window, crazy (not to mention illegal). Taking a guy's sweatshirt when he offers it to you (and maybe even using it as an excuse to call him), normal; keeping a guy's sweatshirt under your pillow for six months without washing it, ill. Just think—would you want someone to follow you, or stare at you, or call your phone and hang up repeatedly? Of course not! Well, guys aren't that different in this respect. So lay off a little. As soon as you stop frightening the boys, they may even start liking you back!

what's your ideal guy type?

There are all kinds of guys out there. And finding the right ones can be hard—especially if you don't know what you're looking for in the first place. That's why we've whipped up this quiz—to cut to the chase. So get ready to discover your dream dude. ♥

1. **Okay, Dating History 101: Your last boyfriend's greatest talent was:**
   a) His creativity. He could play guitar/paint/draw like nobody's business.
   b) Being a total brainiac. He'd ace every school assignment and test. Sometimes without even trying.
   c) His crazy lacrosse moves. When he'd get on the field, nothing—and no one—could keep him from scoring a goal . . . or four.

d) Making crank calls. No matter how many times he called, trying to pass himself off as your kooky guidance counselor, you always fell for it!

e) The way he could always annoy teachers.

2. Of the following, which animal is most appealing to you?
a) Cheetah.
b) Dolphin.
c) Chimpanzee.
d) Horse.
e) Snake.

3. It's movie night at your house! And your mom's offered to bring in some takeout. Which restaurant do you pick?
a) Steve's Steak Shack. Their grub is healthy and hearty, and you love the Hungry Woman's Special.
b) The Garden of Earthly Delights. You've read about the benefits of tofu and wheat grass on the body—and you're a firm believer in the mind-body connection.
c) Ahoy, matey. The fish-and-chips platter isn't all that—but watching that delivery dude climb outta his Corolla in full pirate regalia, now, that's good!
d) The new Malaysian place. You've never had Malaysian before, but you're always up for something new.
e) San Antonio. The enchiladas are *caliente*.

4. Pick and choose your battles. Of the following, select the one combination of qualities (one positive, one negative) that you find the most attractive in guys:
a) Entertaining, immature.

b) Hardworking, reserved.

c) Cool, moody.

d) Imaginative, snobby.

e) Focused, conservative.

5. When your bossy little sister isn't playing Stereo Commando, which radio station do you usually tune in to?

a) The crazy rap-metal one. The one your parents always tell you will destroy your hearing.

b) Top 40, baby! There's nothing like belting out a power ballad to get you pumped!

c) The student-run station of the nearest college. Sure, sometimes their playlists are a little out there, but it beats those lame commercial stations.

d) That talk-fest station. It's all talk, all the time. And a lot of it is hilarious!

e) Listening to the radio is unproductive. You watch *Bill Nye the Science Guy* to get your brain fluids going.

6. It's Friday night, and you're at the school dance. Most likely, your mind is on the guy:

a) In the middle of the dance floor, who's successfully convinced your English teacher to help him lead everyone in The Electric Slide.

b) Onstage, doing a soulful rendition of "Purple Rain."

c) Who's bonding with all his buddies and crushing Coke cans on his forehead—over by the line for the girls' bathroom.

d) Having an intense conversation with his two best friends—a girl and a guy—on the pullout bleachers.

e) Who's at home cramming for his history final—
   between Discovery Channel breaks.

7. **Your parents are letting you repaint your bedroom—any color you want. When you head down to Home Depot, you pick out a can of:**
   a) White. It's classic—and it makes any space look bigger.
   b) Royal blue. It's your school color, so it sets off all your team pics—and your new comforter.
   c) Basic black. To filter out all that pesky sunlight that wakes you up early on the weekend.
   d) Yellow. A color that bright is sure to boost your mood.
   e) Silver. Just like in that cool new music video you saw!

8. **Which quote most resembles your personal mantra?**
   a) "It is better to burn out than it is to rust."
   b) "Real knowledge is to know the extent of one's ignorance."
   c) "A day without laughter is a day wasted."
   d) "I criticize by creation—not by finding fault."
   e) "Just do it!"

9. **You're on a dream date with the perfect guy. What are you doing?**
   a) Skating through the park together, then hitting the big party, where everyone who's anyone will be.
   b) Going to the planetarium for a laser light show—and then out to a romantic dinner for two.
   c) Seeing the latest Jim Carrey movie at the multiplex and laughing so hard that Sprite goes up your nose.

d) Going to the art gallery in his attic, where he unveils
   his latest work . . . a charcoal sketch of you!

e) Sipping a giant Slurpee—with two straws—in the
   parking lot of the Circle K, then hitting the arcade for
   a video game marathon.

10. What would your ideal dude want to do for a living after graduating college?

a) Write for a sitcom.

b) Play on a pro-sports team.

c) Become a professional photographer.

d) Support his freelance writing career by waiting tables.

e) Work for NASA.

scoring

1. a-4, b-1, c-2 , d-3, e-5

2. a-2, b-1, c-3, d-4, e-5

3. a-2, b-5, c-3, d-4, e-1

4. a-3, b-1, c-5, d-4, e-2

5. a-5, b-2, c-4, d-3, e-1

6. a-3, b-5, c-2, d-4, e-1

7. a-1, b-2, c-5, d-3, e-4

8. a-5, b-1, c-3, d-4, e-2

9. a-2, b-1, c-3, d-4, e-5

10. a-3, b-2, c- 4, d-5, e-1,

what's your ideal guy type?

Brainy (10–17)

As far as you're concerned, there's nothing more attractive than a guy who's got a good head on his shoulders. Especially if that head is overflowing with enough knowledge to fill an entire set of World Book encyclopedias! And we think that's cool. Imagine all the deep intellectual conversations you'll have with your Einstein—not to mention all the fun you two can have doing your homework together! So how do you get brainy boy to ask you out? Sign up for an extra-credit history report and spend lots of quality time in the library. And joining the chemistry club couldn't hurt, either!

Sporty (18–25)

You go for the rugged, traditional type. You know, the real meat-'n'-potatoes kinda guy. Most likely, athletics dominate his life—he's probably got a different sport for each season of the year. And chances are, he's no benchwarmer, either. We're guessing he's a standout—if not The Star. Why? Well, he's highly driven and determined—and probably pretty high on the social totem pole to boot. In addition to those qualities, there are other pluses to having a jock for a beau—like instant access to the coolest parties. So practice your cheers, get primped for the pep rally, and prepare to meet your quarterback!

Funny (26–34)

What's life without laughter? That's your mantra. So naturally, the quality you appreciate most in a guy is a killer sense of humor. You're not into those quiet dudes—you're looking for an outgoing guy who can be the class clown, the life of the party, and your own personal Conan O'Brien. We think that's cool—for some girls the stand-up routine could get stale, but you seem to like a guy who's always on. Look for him at the school dance—he'll be the one leading the conga line.

Creative (35–42)

Simply put, artists are your weakness. Whether they're into poetry, painting, or playing music, you just can't resist guys who're inspired to create. There's just something about 'em. Maybe it's their unique vision . . . or maybe it's just the paint-covered Vans. Who knows? It could also be your inner desire to express yourself artfully that's the draw. Whatever the reason, there are lots of ways to hook up with your arty boy—like spending extra time in the school darkroom, signing up for that writing workshop at your community center, and visits to your local art gallery or museum. Voilà!

Alternative (43–50)

You're looking for a dude who breaks the boy-next-door mold. Smashes it, even. Your ideal guy is a poetic James Dean. He might not be a bad boy in the traditional sense, but it's not like he just goes with the flow, either. Sure, he may be misunderstood by some, but he's also undeniably, well, cool. And if you get him and he gets you, that's all that matters. In fact, you two may actually have more in common than you think. Just make sure to wear a helmet if he takes you for a spin on his motorcycle.